"Marry you! You can't be serious, Vincente!"

Dominique couldn't believe her ears.

"Oh, but I am," Vincente said calmly.

Dominique pressed the palms of her hands against her burning cheeks. She felt like a boat that has been forced out of a safe harbor and is being tossed on a wild and alien sea. "This is ridiculous! You don't want to marry me! You don't love me!"

"I want you," he said emotionlessly. "Stop deluding yourself, Dominique! You want me as much as I want you. Why is it that women imagine themselves different from men in that way?"

"You can't marry a person out of lust!" she cried.

"Did I say that was all it was? You know nothing about me, Dominique."

And she knew it was true, just as she knew she could not deny him....

ANNE MATHER

who rides the tiger

Originally published as Harlequin Presents #11

Harlequin Books

TORONTO • LONDON • LOS ANGELES • AMSTERDAM
SYDNEY • HAMBURG • PARIS • STOCKHOLM • ATHENS • TOKYO

Harlequin Presents edition published June 1973
ISBN 0-373-15011-3

Second printing June 1973
Third printing August 1973
Fourth printing November 1973
Fifth printing July 1974
Sixth printing August 1974
Seventh printing April 1976
Eighth printing June 1976
Ninth printing September 1976
Tenth printing February 1977

This *Harlequin Presents Collection* edition published February 1981

Original hardcover edition published in 1970
by Mills & Boon Limited

CHAPTER ONE

THE international airport at Galeao was like all international airports; cool, efficient, but impersonal. Sitting in the airport bar drinking her second glass of Coca-cola, Dominique thought that she might have been anywhere in the world were it not for the predominantly Portuguese accent, and the dark skins of the men around her, who all seemed to find the silvery glint of her hair and the Scandinavian blue of her eyes rather arresting.

Sighing, she glanced again at her watch, wondering how much longer she was going to have to wait. The message which had been handed to her on her arrival had been less than explicit. It had merely stated that John had been unavoidably delayed, and would she wait at the airport if he was not there to meet her as arranged.

She lit a cigarette, conceded a slight smile to the youth who had been eyeing her avidly for the last half hour, and drew on it deeply. It was difficult not to feel impatient even though she knew that Bela Vista was some distance inland. After all, John had known for over a week the date and time of her arrival, so surely he could have arranged to stay overnight in Rio, rather than leave her waiting at the airport for an indefinite period.

Since arriving she had taken advantage of every facility the airport offered. She had visited the ladies' room and showered and changed into a cool cotton shift, much more suitable to the heat outside the air-conditioned walls of the airport buildings than the mohair suit she had been wearing when she left London thirty-six hours ago. She had done her hair, taking time to loop it into the rather sophisticated style

John preferred, and she had applied a light make-up to the smooth, creamy skin of her face, accentuating the curve of her cheeks and the curling length of her lashes. But now, as time wore on, she was beginning to wish she hadn't bothered. She had explored the airport shops for genuine examples of Brazilian wood-carvings, had a meal, a modest European meal, in the airport restaurant, and had finally taken refuge in the airport bar, hoping her stay would be short-lived.

Earlier in the day when the giant Boeing had circled Galeao prior to landing excitement had held her in its thrall. There were so many exciting landmarks to see and exclaim at: the gentle Sugar Loaf mountain, and the peak of Corcovado with its vast statue of Christ, standing arms outstretched, as though encompassing the whole sweep of Guanabara Bay. The peaks beyond these two were so jagged and impressive that she almost lost sight of the white smear of Copacabana beach, faced by the skyscraper hotels that are such a violent contrast to the *favellas*, those slums that cling to the hillsides around Rio. She had sensed the atmosphere and known instinctively that all the weeks of waiting had been worthwhile. It was incredible to imagine that soon she would see John again, feel his arms around her, and find that security in his presence that had attracted her to him in the first place. The dismay she had felt when he had first announced he was going to work in Brazil had all disappeared, to be replaced with a sense of gratitude that through him she was to see a little more of the world. But six months ago, when he left England, she had still been in the process of recovering from the death of her beloved father, and maybe that was why she had been unable to look ahead with any degree of confidence.

Her mother had died many years ago, when she was only a baby, and her father had become the mainstay of her existence. That he should be killed on his way to attend a patient had seemed doubly painful, particularly as that patient had been one of his 'regulars', a man convinced he was capable of contracting every tiny ailment that might be about. But Doctor Mallory had never neglected to answer any call, and in the blanketing fog in which London had been wrapped that evening it had been only too easy to collide with another vehicle. For weeks Dominique had been numb with grief, unable to believe that her father was dead and she was alone in the world. There were distant relatives, an aunt and uncle and some cousins in the north of England, but Dominique had not wanted to share her grief with strangers who at the most could offer sympathy.

It was during these weeks of misery that she had first met John Harding. John was the son of Adam Harding, her father's solicitor and close friend, and he had recently returned from the Middle East where he had been working in the laboratory of an oil company. He was a pleasantly attractive young man, in his late twenties, and Dominique was attracted by the warmth and gentleness of his manner.

Aware of her recent bereavement, John had gently prised her out of the shell she had wrapped about herself, and endeavoured to show her that life went on in the same way as it had always done. At first, Dominique was reluctant, unwilling to allow anyone to witness the painful apathy that possessed her. But gradually, in John's presence, she began to smile again, to live again.

The worst part of all had been finding another job. She had always acted as her father's receptionist and of course although another doctor was to take over the practice she couldn't bear the thought of continuing in that capacity. It was John who found her another position. He had a colleague, a dentist in fact, who was looking for an attractive young woman to take charge of his records, do a little

7

typing, and admit his patients. Dominique had accepted the job gladly, and when the house in which she and her father had spent so many happy years was sold she allowed John to find her a flat.

Adam Harding had encouraged their friendship, and Dominique knew that he and his wife were hoping that this friendship would blossom into something more binding. Dominique, who had always thought herself so self-confident, found it was very pleasant allowing someone else to do all her thinking for her, and when John obtained a position in a laboratory in London, she was content to allow her life to drift along smoothly.

However, after several months, John was offered another position – in Brazil.

Dominique was horrified. Somehow, she had imagined John would always work in England now, and sooner or later it was taken for granted they would get married. John's parents were as keen as he was, and probably in other circumstances, if Dominique had not so recently lost her father they might already have been married. But the job in Brazil demanded an immediate decision, and although John was eager that she should go with him, as his wife, Dominique hesitated, too uncertain still to do anything impulsively. So they got engaged, and it had been agreed that as soon as John was settled there, and had an apartment suitable to accommodate a wife, Dominique should join him and they would get married in Brazil. Naturally, John's parents were a little disappointed that they would not be at the wedding, but they understood Dominique's situation.

During the weeks after John's departure Dominique had suffered many pangs of regret that she had not taken the plunge and gone with him, but eventually she orientated herself to her new circumstances, and began to enjoy life again. She made friends with the two girls who lived in the adjacent flat to her own and went out with them from time to time, to the cinema or the theatre, and sometimes even to a party. Every week she visited the Hardings and most week-ends she spent with them, either visiting their country cottage in Wiltshire, or going down to Sussex to see their daughter who was married with three children of her own. Dominique adored the children and she felt an immense sense of gratitude to the Hardings for providing so many diversions to fill her days so that her life with her father was not a painful thing to recall, but rather a pleasant feeling of nostalgia. With their help she had erased the hopelessness which had engulfed her at the time of his death.

John wrote quite eagerly, his letters long and descriptive, providing Dominique with a pictorial record of his life in South America. She learned of the contrasts of the country where she was soon to live; the painful poverty and excessive wealth of its people, the extremes of climate it possessed, but most dramatic of all its savage beauty that assaulted the eyes and gripped the senses. Already Dominique felt familiar with the country, and with Bela Vista in particular, the area where John was living and working. This community was composed of a mixture of nationalities including North Americans, Germans and British, as well as the Brazilians themselves. The oil company was owned by the Santos Corporation who presently employed John, and according to his letters it was quite a large concern.

Dominique glanced at her watch. She had adjusted it to the local time scale, and it read a little after four-thirty. As her plane had landed at eleven that morning she was naturally becoming a little disturbed at the delay. Surely if John was going to be so late he could have suggested that she book herself into a hotel overnight and thus alleviate these hours of waiting?

She was in the process of deciding whether or not to order a third glass of Coca-cola when she became aware that a man was scrutinizing her very intently from a table half-way across the room. She gave him a cool quelling stare, but it produced no result that she could see. Instead, he lifted his glass of spirit from the table and tipping his chair back on two legs surveyed her rather appraisingly.

Really, she thought impatiently, this was too much!

Sliding off the bar-stool on which she had been perched, she lifted her overnight case and marched purposefully towards the door. However, she was forced to pass the man's table and despite her annoyance at his insolence she could not resist taking a second look at him. He was certainly one of the most attractive men she had ever seen – dark-haired and dark-skinned, with eyes of a strange light tawny colour that gave her a rather mocking stare as she passed. He was lean, with hard features that she thought could look almost cruel on occasions. He seemed to epitomize all that was alien and unfamiliar and dangerous in this alien, unfamiliar and dangerous country. She shivered, and pushing open the door emerged into the wide reception hall.

Sighing, she looked about her, praying for a sight of John. Didn't he realize how strange and nervous she was bound to feel here? What could possibly have delayed him for so long? Surely he couldn't have had an accident! Could he?

She walked across the hall and seated herself on one of the comfortable chairs, and taking out her cigarettes she lit one, drawing on it deeply. Tapping her fingers on the arm of the chair, she was absorbed with her own anxieties and was unaware of anyone approaching her until a deep, masculine voice said:

'You are Miss Mallory, are you not? Miss Dominique Mallory?'

Dominique started, and her eyes widened as she looked up into the face of the man from the bar.

Recovering her composure, she said, with as much coolness as she could muster: 'You know my name?'

The man stood before her, regarding her almost derisively, his hands thrust deep into the pockets of the trousers of the immaculate dark silk suit he was wearing.

'There are not too many unescorted English women filling in time at Galeao,' he remarked lazily.

Dominique stubbed out her cigarette and got to her feet. She felt at less of a disadvantage that way. Even so, despite her own height, he was still much taller than she was.

'Please be more explicit,' she said, trying to sound cold and aloof, and failing.

He shrugged. 'Of course, Miss Mallory. Forgive me for wasting your most valuable time!' He was mocking her again. 'My name is Vincente Santos. I am a – shall we say – colleague of you fiancé's.'

Dominique relaxed a little. 'Oh, I see,' she exclaimed. 'Is John not coming after all?'

'Unfortunately no. He has been delayed. I will explain more fully in a few moments. Is this all your luggage?'

Dominique hesitated, glanced down at her case, and rubbed her nose thoughtfully. 'Er – do you – I mean – have you any means of identification?'

The man half-smiled. 'You do not trust me?'

Dominique compressed her lips. He was making it very difficult for her.

'It's not you in particular, you understand,' she said hastily. 'Only you might be anybody. You could easily have heard my name from one of the airport officials, and – well. . . .' She spread her hands expressively.

The man shrugged his broad shoulders. 'You are right, of course, Miss Mallory,' he replied, with a slight bow of his head. 'It is always safer to take precautions. However, I can assure you I am who I say I am. There is only one Vincente Santos!'

Dominique stared at him. Was he serious? Really, the conceit of the man!

'Don't you have any papers?' she asked stiffly. 'A driver's licence, perhaps?'

Vincente Santos patiently withdrew his wallet from his pocket and produced a passport and an international driving licence. Dominique barely glanced at them, certain that no would-be abductor could be so sure of himself.

'Thank you,' she said, glancing down at her case. 'This is all my luggage. My other cases were sent independently.'

Vincente Santos nodded, and putting away his wallet bent and lifted the case. 'Come with me,' he said, and strode away across the hall so that Dominique had almost to run to keep up with him.

Outside the airport buildings the heat hit her like an actual physical force, and she gasped. The air-conditioning inside had not prepared her for this. Santos glanced her way.

'This is cooler than in the middle of the day,' he remarked. 'You'll soon get used to it.'

Dominique managed a faint smile. Already she was wishing that John had asked someone else to meet her. Someone who was less blatantly attractive and sure of himself. With Vincente Santos she felt at a disadvantage, and despite the fact that he was faultlessly polite, she had the feeling that he was merely amusing himself at her expense.

A sleek green convertible awaited them outside the airport, and Vincente Santos threw her case unceremoniously into the back, and then opened the door for her to climb in. Dominique slid in and waited for him to join her, taking in the delicious perfumes of a positive riot of flowers that grew beside the paved car park. The colours were brilliant and various and she felt an unwilling shiver of excitement slide along her spine. Towering above were the ragged peaks of the Serras, and away in the distance the blue wash of the Atlantic. It was exotic and exhilarating after the greyness of London, and even Santos's lazy tolerance seemed to lose some of its mockery.

He climbed in beside her, saw her expressive face, and smiled, revealing even white teeth that contrasted sharply with the dark tan of his features.

'You have not been to Brazil before?' he murmured, turning the ignition.

Dominique shook her head. 'No.'

'But already you feel the pulse of our country,' he remarked casually, and drove the car out of the parking area.

Dominique liked his expression. That was exactly how she did feel. The excitement which had gripped her before the plane landed was returning, and with it a sense of awareness of her surroundings. There was something primitive and untamed about the country, even with its soaring skyscrapers and luxury apartments. How could anyone forget that the Matto Grosso was not too far away with its impenetrable forests and dangerous rivers where a man could be lost without trace? Just another of the facets of a country as complex as its history. Maybe it was that sense of the unknown that thrilled her so. Like the impetus that drove a man to risk his life to discover the savagery of primitive civilizations.

She became aware that Vincente Santos was speaking to her and endeavoured to orientate herself to her present situation.

'You used to live in London, I believe,' he was saying.

Dominique nodded. 'That's right. At least, in the suburbs.

Tell me, why didn't John come to meet me? And where are we going now?'

He smiled again. 'I was beginning to think you had forgotten the purpose for your visit here,' he remarked lazily. And then: 'Bela Vista where you are to live is in these mountains, but the roads are not to be recommended. They are little more than tracks in places. Do not imagine though that Bela Vista is an uncivilized place. It has its museum and its art gallery and its university. But to get there – ah, that is another matter.'

Dominique wrinkled her nose. 'Go on.'

He shrugged expressively. 'There was a landslide on the road.'

Dominique gasped. 'Was – was anyone hurt?'

'No. But your fiancé was – what do you say? – stranded. So he telephoned me.'

'You – you were in Rio?' questioned Dominique slowly.

'No, I was in Bela Vista.'

Dominique gave an exasperated sigh. 'Please, Mr. Santos, don't tease me. How could you get here and not John?'

Vincente Santos swung the car round a precipitous bend in the road, causing Dominique to cling apprehensively to her seat, and then said: 'I have other means of transport. A helicopter!'

'Oh! Oh, I see!' Dominique nodded. 'I naturally assumed. . . .' She shrugged. 'Do you live in Bela Vista, Mr. Santos?'

'I live in many places,' he replied enigmatically. 'But I do have a house at Bela Vista, yes.'

Dominique digested this, and as she did so she wondered whether he might be John's employer. After all, the names were the same, but Santos was a common enough name in Brazil. If this man was part of the organization what was his connection with her fiancé? How well did he know John, and conversely, how well did John know him? There were a hundred questions she wanted to ask but couldn't. Instead, she said:

'Are we going to Bela Vista now?'

'The road is blocked,' he reminded her patiently.

'I know. I meant of course by helicopter.'

He looked rather sardonic, causing a faint flush to colour Dominique's cheeks. She was intensely aware of him, and it did not make for relaxation. He was the kind of man of whom she knew nothing. There was a sensual line to his mouth which disturbed her a little. He was obviously used to the company of women, and it was annoying to realize that she hadn't the faintest idea of how to deal with him. It wasn't only the alien cast of his features, or the fact that his clothes and car and whole attitude depicted wealth of a kind she had never before experienced, it was something else, something indefinable that made him different from any other man she had ever known. And it was infuriating to know that he was aware of his attraction, and probably of how she reacted to him. Stiffening her shoulders, she said briskly: 'What do you intend doing with me?'

He gave a lazy laugh. 'Doing with you, Miss Mallory? That's a curious expression. What do you imagine I am going to do with you?' The car curved over a promontory and below them was spread the land-locked harbour of Rio de Janeiro, with Guanabara Bay beyond, studded with islands that glistened like jewels in the rays of the sinking sun.

Dominique stared entranced for a few moments, and then gathering her thoughts, she said briefly: 'You must know what I mean!'

He inclined his head, the wheel of the car sliding through the hard strength of his brown fingers. 'Yes, I know. And I realize you are eager to meet your fiancé again. After all, it is some time since he left England, and a lot can happen in only a few months. However, it will be dark soon now and I do not care to risk putting down the helicopter among these mountains in darkness.'

Dominique twisted the strap of her handbag. 'So?'

'So I regret to tell you that you must spend this night in Rio. A room has been booked for you at a hotel there where you will be very comfortable, and tomorrow – well, tomorrow you will be able to cast yourself into the arms of your beloved!'

Dominique gave him a hard stare. 'Thank you,' she said, coldly. 'I don't need you to give me instructions!'

'I'm sure you don't,' he agreed mockingly, allowing his gaze to slide over her so that she flushed uncomfortably in spite of herself.

Then he frowned: 'You still distrust me, don't you, Miss Mallory? Why?'

Dominique sighed. 'I didn't say that!'

'No,' he remarked. 'It is your whole attitude. Perhaps you think I have kidnapped you. When you reach the hotel you will be able to speak to Harding on the telephone.'

The telephone, thought Dominique with relief. Of course! Why hadn't she thought of that?

Vincente Santos was still giving her a slightly sardonic look. 'You are a beautiful woman, Miss Mallory, but I regret to tell you I have known many beautiful women, and in my experience I do not have to kidnap them to make them submit!'

Dominique could not have felt more embarrassed, and it was with relief that she saw the outer environs of the city appearing. Even so, she was unprepared for the poverty and squalor of some of those dwellings which were little more than shacks, their occupants looking little better, with thin angular bodies and dirty faces. Her horror at these revelations must have communicated itself to him, for he said:

'Where there are very rich there are also very poor. You are like everyone else, Miss Mallory. You want to see only what you expect to see.'

Dominique looked at him. 'And how do you see it, Mr. Santos? Or perhaps you do not see it at all?'

Vincente Santos's expression darkened. 'Oh, I see it, Miss Mallory!'

Dominique glanced at him. There was a bitterness in his voice that was different from the casual amusement that had been there before. Then he said: 'You imagine perhaps that I have only known this kind of life, this affluence, perhaps?'

Dominique bit her lip. 'I didn't think about it, Mr. Santos.'

'Then perhaps you should think before you speak,' he said, somewhat bleakly, and she wondered what unknowing spark she had ignited.

The city of Rio de Janeiro was unbelievably beautiful. Even Venice, which she had visited with her father, had not the individuality of architecture that Rio possessed in such abundance. Or maybe it was the grim overhanging buttresses of the Serras that brought such grandeur to an otherwise contemporary scene. The streets were thronged with cars and people and the noise was deafening. There was a predominance of young people, dressed casually in beach clothes. The girls in their bikinis and the young men with their sun-bronzed torsos resembled nothing so much as the high priests and priestesses who worshipped at the shrine of the Sun-god. Dominique saw old dowagers dressed entirely in black, like old crows in their severity among birds of paradise. There were dozens of children, ragged urchins with filthy faces, but so dark and attractive that they drew the eye. There were churches and museums, and tall sky-scraper buildings, among streets lined with trees and paved in black and white mosaic.

The hotel Vincente Santos drove to stood in a quiet side-street, off the main thoroughfare near the centre of the city. The hotel was tall and handsome, grey-stoned and respect-able, not one of the monolithic palaces that faced the beach at Copacabana. It had a strange kind of old-world charm that was in variance to the almost blatant modernity of its neighbours. Yet despite its appearance inside it was modern, with lifts and wall-to-wall carpeting. Dominique was to learn that to Brazilians wall-to-wall carpeting was con-sidered extremely desirable, even if it did make bedrooms stiflingly hot.

The car was left in the car-park and they entered the hotel, Vincente Santos going ahead to speak to the recep-tionist. From the amount of deference he received Domi-nique gathered he was a valued client, and she hovered near the swing doors, unwilling to interfere. Then he turned and said:

'Your room is ready. I expect you are tired and would like to shower and change before dinner. It will be served in the restaurant any time after seven-thirty. Harding has already telephoned to question your arrival, and will ring you back later, I imagine. I do not think there is anything else—'

Dominique linked her fingers. Somehow now that he ap-peared to have discharged his duty she was loath to let him go. Perhaps it was the strangeness of everything and this sense she had of being completely alone, but she hesitated uncertainly, wishing they could have left for Bela Vista right away.

Vincente Santos moved towards the door. He moved with a sinuous feline grace, like a tiger, the muscles across his back rippling smoothly beneath the thin material of his suit.

And like his counterpart in the animal kingdom Dominique realized he could be dangerous. She didn't quite know how she knew this. Certainly his manner towards her had not suggested the predatory male; even so he had spent several minutes staring at her in the airport bar when he must have known full well who she was, and she shivered slightly at the recollection. He looked back at her as he reached the doors.

'You are satisfied?' he asked smoothly.

'Of course.' Dominique was hasty. Whatever her feelings she had no intention of letting him realize her uncertainty.

'That is good. I will pick you up at ten in the morning. Good night, Miss Mallory.'

'Good – good night, Mr. Santos.' Dominique was conscious of a page picking up the case which Vincente Santos had stood beside her, and then he gave a brief nod and disappeared through the swing doors.

'This way, *senhorita*,' said the page in heavily accented English, and Dominique recalled that Vincente Santos had had little accent. Then she gave the page a faint smile and followed him across to the lift.

Her rooms were spacious and luxurious, with many windows overlooking the city. She could not see the *favellas* from here, and despite the noise of the traffic in the distance it was peaceful. A fan whirred lazily causing a cooling draught of air and the water in the shower was lukewarm.

Afterwards, she lay on her bed, staring at the telephone, willing it to ring. Maybe if she could hear John's voice she could dispel the feeling of anxiety which seemed to have taken possession of her.

CHAPTER TWO

SHE must have fallen asleep, for when she opened her eyes the telephone was ringing, and the room was dark apart from the lights from outside in the street. Shivering slightly, she leaned over and switched on the bedside lamp. It revealed a cream-coloured telephone beside the bed, and as she lifted the receiver she glanced at her watch. Eight-fifteen! It couldn't be!

Then she said: 'Hello, Dominique Mallory speaking.'

'Dominique! Is that you? Oh, thank heaven!' John sounded relieved and anxious. 'How are you, love? I'm sorry I had to leave you in the lurch at the airport. Did Santos explain?'

'Yes, of course, John.' Dominique wriggled into a sitting position. 'Oh, it's marvellous to hear your voice after all this time. I'm fine. The hotel is very comfortable.'

'Good, good. Have you had dinner?'

'Actually no. I must have fallen asleep,' exclaimed Dominique, with a laugh. 'But I'm ravenous now. Looking forward to seeing you. Has the landslide been cleared yet?'

'Cleared? You must be joking! Things don't move at that pace round here. Landslides can take anything from a week to a month to be cleared.'

'Oh, I see.'

'Why? You're not nervous about coming in on the chopper, are you?' John sounded worried. 'Santos is a good pilot.'

'No – of course not.' Dominique reached for her cigarettes. 'Tell me, John, who is this man Santos? Is he something to do with your company?'

'Yeah. His father founded the corporation, actually.'

'I see. So he's your boss, then?'

'Heck, no! Vincente Santos doesn't worry over-much about the corporation. He's far too busy spending the money it earns!' John sounded slightly bitter.

Dominique frowned. 'You don't sound as though you like him.'

'Santos?' John snorted. 'We have nothing in common. As for not liking him, that's quite an understatement. But as he hates my guts, too, I'm not too worried about that!'

Dominique felt disturbed. She had never heard John talk this way before. 'Then – then how come he was the only person you could ask to meet me?' she exclaimed.

'Helicopters are not two a penny,' remarked John dryly. 'Besides, when I phoned in about the landslide someone else asked him to come. He was the logical person to ask in the circumstances.'

'I see.' Dominique digested this. 'What – what are you doing now?' She lit her cigarette. 'Where are you phoning from?'

'My apartment. You'll like it, Dom. It's in one of the new blocks and it's spacious. I've not got much furniture yet. I'm leaving that to you. You're to stay with the Rawlings like I wrote you. I've fixed the wedding for five weeks hence. That will give you time to get acclimatized and also time to get what you want for the apartment. We have some good stores and Mrs. Rawlings has said you can borrow her sewing machine to run up curtains and such like.'

Dominique drew on her cigarette. 'It doesn't seem real somehow,' she said, shaking her head. 'I mean – being here – in Brazil!'

John laughed. 'That's natural. You've just flown several thousand miles. It takes time for your mind to catch up with your body!'

'I suppose that's what it is,' she nodded.

'Well, anyway, roll on tomorrow. Phones are such inadequate things when I'm longing to see you and hold you and kiss you.' John's voice was husky. 'I love you, Dom!'

'And I love you, John,' she murmured.

'I'll go now, then. Go have some dinner and then have an early night. You must be exhausted!'

'Not now. I've just had about three hours' rest. But I will go and get some dinner. Will you meet me when we land, John?'

'Of course. G'bye, honey.'

'Good-bye, John.'

After he had rung off she sat staring at the telephone for several minutes. It was strange how different John sounded now from the man she had known in England. Or maybe he didn't sound any different, she was just hearing him differently.

She sighed and stubbed her cigarette out in a brass ashtray. She had the strongest suspicion that she should not have had these six months away from John. What if they had both changed? What if her opinion of him was different now that he was taken out of his normal environment?

But that was ridiculous. If you loved somebody, you loved them no matter what. You didn't change because of circumstances or environment.

She slid off the bed and opened her overnight case. Apart from the suit she had been wearing when she left London and which she had changed at the airport there was a navy blue uncrushable shift which she had packed for her first night at Bela Vista to save her tackling her other trunks. Taking it out, she laid it on the bed and then sluiced her face before applying a light make-up. Her lashes were naturally long and she darkened them with a little mascara, smoothing some eye-shadow on to the lids. Then she applied a pale lipstick and wriggled into the navy shift. Her hair was thick and long and heavy, but she couldn't be bothered to attempt a sophisticated knot, so she added an Alice band which kept it back off her face. Then she left her room and took the lift down to the restaurant.

At this hour of the evening it was not too busy and the waiter showed her deferentially to a table. Maybe he thought she was some close friend of Vincente Santos, she thought dryly. Certainly she had never experienced such obsequious attention before. She chose a dish comprising beef, black beans and rice, which while being rather rich and spicy, was rather delicious. Then she had an orange dessert, with real fresh oranges that somehow tasted different from the ones she was used to eating back in England, and finished with cheese and coffee.

'You enjoyed the meal, *senhorita*?' It was the head waiter bowing beside the table.

Dominique flicked ash from the end of her cigarette and nodded enthusiastically. 'Thank you. It was delicious!'

'I am very happy. Perhaps a liqueur with your coffee? Brandy perhaps?'

Dominique shook her head regretfully. 'Oh, really, no. The wine with the meal was quite enough for me. I don't have a strong head for alcohol.' She offered the explanation with a smile.

'Are you endeavouring to lead the innocent into temptation, my friend?' remarked a deep voice lazily, and Dominique looked up, startled, to see Vincente Santos standing behind the head waiter, looking dark and lean and disturbingly masculine in a dark dinner suit.

The head waiter glanced round and smiled with real pleasure. 'Ah, Senhor Santos,' he said, nodding. 'You startled me. I was merely offering the young lady a liqueur, but she seems unwilling to accept.'

Vincente Santos moved round the table, pulling out a chair and straddling it lazily. 'So, Miss Mallory. You are afraid to take any risks, is that right?'

Dominique controlled her blushes with difficulty. 'I didn't say that, Mr. Santos. I don't have a head for spirits, that's all.'

'But that is sad!' he mocked her gently. 'Particularly as I know my good friend Enrico here possesses some of the finest brandy in the whole of Brazil.' He looked up at the head waiter. 'The *senhorita* will drink with me later, Enrico. You may go.'

'*Sim, senhor.*' The waiter left them, and Vincente Santos gave her an appraising glance.

'You look very charming, Miss Mallory. It seems a shame to waste such beauty on the restaurant of the Maria Magdalena.'

Dominique felt her nerves jumping. She was quite sure he wasn't seriously suggesting that he had come here for any other purpose than to ascertain that she was being adequately looked after.

'What would you suggest, Mr. Santos?' she parried coolly, endeavouring to appear composed while her stomach was churning with suppressed excitement.

Vincente Santos smiled. 'What would I suggest? Well – let me see – I know a night club, called the Piranha, where we could dance, and there is a good cabaret.'

Dominique shivered. 'Piranha? Aren't they the fish that can destroy a living creature in minutes?'

'That's right.' His reply was laconic. 'I'm not considering offering you as a sacrifice, Miss Mallory.'

Dominique bit her lip. 'You have relieved my mind,' she retorted quickly. 'However, as I'm quite sure you're not seriously suggesting that we spend the rest of the evening together, I'll wish you good night again.' She got to her feet, but he rose also, blocking her way.

'You do not think I am serious?' he questioned. 'Why? Surely, entertaining the fiancée of my colleague is the least I can do in the circumstances.'

'You are hardly a colleague of my fiancé,' returned Dominique quietly, looking down at her handbag.

'Ah! You have spoken to the good fellow!' he said sardonically. 'And has he warned you against me?'

'Of course not. Why should he do that?' Dominique made a movement. 'Please – excuse me!'

'In a moment. Do you object to my asking for your company?'

Dominique sighed. 'Of course not.'

'But you refuse?'

Dominique gave a helpless movement of her shoulders. 'Mr. Santos, it may amuse you to make fun of me, but I'm growing a little tired of it. Excuse me.'

Vincente Santos moved aside. 'I was mistaken, obviously,' he said indifferently. 'I had thought you looked lonely.'

Dominique looked up at him in exasperation. 'So you took pity on me?'

'Hardly that. However, I am quite prepared to show you a little of the cultural capital of my country.'

Dominique took a step, hesitated, and glanced back at him. 'It was very kind of you,' she said awkwardly. 'And – I would like to have seen a little more of the city.'

'Yet you still hesitate. Am I such a terrifying person? Does the prospect of a few hours in my company repel you so?'

Dominique smiled. 'You know perfectly well that you are deliberately misunderstanding me,' she said.

He came round the table to her side, looking down at her intently. His fingers stroked the bare skin of her forearm

25

almost absently. 'As I said before, Miss Mallory, you are a beautiful young woman, and I should like to take you to the Piranha.'

Dominique felt the muscles of her arm tense beneath his casual touch. Her breathing seemed difficult, and there was a trembling sensation somewhere near her knees. Was he aware of the effect he was having on her? He didn't seem so, but that was no guide. For all his urbanity his innermost thoughts were enigmatic, this she sensed.

She tried to shrug these thoughts away. She must be crazy, allowing him to disturb her so. It was too long since she had seen John, known the company of a man. She was behaving like a schoolgirl. Why didn't she just refuse his offer point blank and go back to her room? That was what she ought to do, what John would expect her to do. Why then did the prospect seem so dreary? Had the sleep she had had destroyed any further chance of rest for some time? Why couldn't she feel pleasantly tired instead of vigorously alive?

'I really think I must refuse,' she murmured reluctantly.

Vincente Santos lifted his shoulders, the fine material of his suit gleaming in the artificial light. His thin face wore that slightly cruel expression as he said accusingly: 'You're afraid, Miss Mallory!'

She could have agreed with him, she was afraid, and she wasn't quite sure of what.

'Don't be ridiculous!' she snapped.

'Then come with me. Prove I'm wrong!' he taunted her.

Dominique's fingers tortured the strap of her handbag. 'All right, Mr. Santos. All right, since you insist, I'll come with you.'

'Good.' His fingers gripped her arm, guiding her across

the almost deserted room. 'I admire your courage!'

Dominique wrenched her arm out of his grasp. 'One doesn't need courage, Mr. Santos. Only fortitude!'

But he just laughed at this, and she could have hit him.

Rio at night was a magical place, lit with a million electric bulbs. The traffic was just as congested, but now music could be heard from every street corner, and the rhythm of the guitar beat into Dominique's brain like some seductive drug. The Piranha was near Copacabana, a huge neon-lighted building with a brilliant decor that was toned down by discreet lighting. It was the kind of place Dominique had always abhorred, following her father's tastes in music, and later John's. But with Vincente Santos she saw it through different eyes.

There were several rooms; in one you could dance, in another drink, in another eat, and in yet another gamble. Dividing the rooms were aquariums filled with a variety of species, and only in the foyer was there a huge tank of the fish that gave the club its name. Dominique shivered when she saw them, and Vincente Santos said:

'They can reduce a man to a skeleton in minutes, did you know that?'

Dominique wrinkled her nose. 'I did know, as a matter of fact,' she said. 'Devil fish!'

'Hmm.' He slid an arm around her shoulders casually. 'Come on, we'll have a drink.'

'Just tomato juice for me, please,' she said, uncomfortably aware of his arm, and walking just a little quicker so that he had to drop it.

However when he handed her a drink a few moments later it was certainly not tomato juice. 'Heavens, what's this?' she gasped at the tall glass of liquid.

'My own recipe. Taste it!'

She did so, and found it was delicious. It seemed to be lime and perhaps lemon, with something else added, something that certainly gave it a lift. Deciding that one drink couldn't possibly harm her, she accepted a cigarette and they walked into the room where a cabaret was taking place on the dance floor.

There was a Brazilian fire-eater followed by a Portuguese guitarist who sang quite appealingly. Dominique sipped her drink, smoked her cigarette, and listened to the cacophony of sound around her. There was a mixture of accents, from Portuguese and Spanish to pure North American. She heard the guttural sound of a German voice, followed by a very British accent, and she glanced at Vincente Santos. He was watching her. He seemed to be constantly watching her, she thought, and it embarrassed her. She had never experienced such intense appraisal before.

'Must you?' she asked.

'Must I what?'

'Stare at me.'

'Why not? I like staring at you.'

Faced with such candour, Dominique was at a loss for a reply, and he said: 'Leave your drink here. Let's dance.'

The cabaret was over and the band was beginning to play. The music from guitars, organs and drums was vibrant and pulsating with rhythm, and the lights were lowered as couples gathered on the dance floor.

'I don't. That is—' she began, as he took her hand and drew her through the tables where people were sitting to the far end of the room.

'You don't what?' he asked softly, as he turned and slid his arms around her, pulling her close against the hard muscular strength of his body.

Dominique shook her head. With Vincente's eyes upon her, so near now, she found it difficult to think coherently.

'I've never danced to beat music before,' she confessed. 'I'm quite a square really.'

He gave a soft laugh. 'Oh, Miss Mallory, whatever gave you that idea?'

They moved slowly, and Dominique found after all that it was easy to follow Vincente's movements. Besides, the dancing seemed of secondary importance to their actual situation. If John could see me now, she thought, a trifle wildly. He would be absolutely astounded! And with good reason, she added silently. She had known what kind of a man Vincente Santos was from the moment she saw him watching her in the airport bar. Why then had she succumbed to the temptation of going out with him? Was it because all her life she had thought before acting, never doing anything on impulse? Or was it simply because the strength of his personality and the way he had taunted her had aroused her indignation, and she had wanted to prove she could be as impulsive as anyone else? Certainly he made the men she had met back in England seem a trifle tame by comparison, and there was an addictive sense of excitement in taking such risks. After all, tonight would soon be over and then she would be with John again, and Vincente Santos would fade into obscurity.

Once, while they danced, she glanced up at him, her hair brushing his cheek, and he looked down at her with his tawny eyes, eyes that seemed too penetrating, and his mouth was very close to hers. Hastily, she looked down again, endeavouring to control the fast beating of her heart. So far and no further, she told herself firmly.

The dance was soon over, and as they were leaving the floor they were halted by an excited cry from a woman who was also leaving the dance floor with her escort. Tall and slender, with jet black hair piled high with jewelled combs into a French knot, she was easily the most beautiful and exotic creature that Dominique had ever seen. Her gown, a long clinging affair of heavy crêpe which moulded her perfect body, was in a brilliant shade of red, and it contrasted vividly with her magnolia colouring and dark hair.

'Vincente!' she exclaimed, flinging her arms about his neck and kissing him rapidly on both cheeks and then lingeringly on his mouth. 'But I did not know you were in Rio! Why did you not let me know? I have been back two weeks from Europe, and I am desolate. You have not been to see me!'

Vincente glanced at Dominique over the woman's head, seeing her embarrassment, and then disentangling himself firmly.

'I have been busy, Sophia,' he said, his voice cool, so that the woman looked at Dominique and gave her a studious glance.

'Oh, yes,' she said questioningly. 'I can see you have. I would have thought she was a little young and unsophisticated for your tastes, my sweet!'

Vincente's eyes darkened. 'Did I ask for your opinion, Sophia?' he remarked icily.

'No. But then I feel I have the right to voice my inmost thoughts to you. After all, you invariably come back, *chéri*!'

Dominique turned away, sickened by this exchange. She made her way back to their table, and re-seated herself, wishing she had the courage to walk out of the night club. But outside was a strange alien city and she didn't much fancy trying to get a taxi alone at this time of night.

A few moments later a shadow fell across the table and she looked up into Vincente's dark face. 'Do not do that again,' he snapped.

'Do what? Leave you to your mistress?' she exclaimed,

stung by his assumption that he had the right to dictate her affairs.

He caught her wrist and wrenched her up out of her seat. 'Come,' he said. 'We will go somewhere else.'

Dominique struggled uselessly. 'I want to go home, Mr. Santos,' she said coldly. 'At least – back to my hotel!'

He did not reply, but merely turned and walked out of the restaurant, practically dragging her along behind him.

Outside the night air was warm and velvety, and millions of stars twinkled overhead, vying with the myriad strings of lights that edged the promenade adjacent to Copacabana beach. The sound of the ceaseless surf was like thunder in their ears, and Dominique took several deep breaths to rid her lungs of the smoky atmosphere of the club.

They reached the car, and he put her inside firmly, and then walked round to get in beside her. He flicked the ignition, and the powerful engine roared to life, and they drove out of the parking area and along the sea front. Presently he turned off into the winding side streets, steep thoroughfares that wound round the older buildings of the city. Dominique wanted to ask where he was taking her, but his expression brooked no interference and she kept silent, wishing with all her heart she had never been foolish enough to come out with him.

Eventually they emerged from the side streets into a wide avenue of trees, and he drove along this towards a park at the far end. Near the park were several blocks of luxury apartments, and it was into the forecourt of one of these apartment buildings that he drove. He halted the car, pocketed the keys, and helped Dominique out. She looked up at the block fearfully, and then at Vincente.

'Come,' he said, and she had no choice but to follow him.

Inside several lifts transported the tenants to their as-

31

signed destination, and it was into one of these that he drew her. He pressed the button for the penthouse, and the lift shot up silently. Dominique barely had time to collect herself before they were stepping out into a wide carpeted hall. Vincente closed the lift doors, pressed a button, and it glided away. Then he took Dominique's arm and led her towards double panelled doors.

Producing his keys, he flung open one of the doors, and gently urged her inside. When he switched on the lights, Dominique just stood and stared. She had never seen such luxury in all her life.

Shallow steps led down into the body of the room on to a floor that was tiled in mosaic of blue and gold, an iridescent kind of mosaic that glinted in the artificial lights. Skin rugs adorned this floor, echoed in the seats of deep armchairs which were otherwise made of black leather. Almost a whole wall had been given over to a window that gave a panoramic view of the city, fitted with a venetian blind that could be adjusted to admit light but not the dazzling sunshine. Tonight it was open and even from the doorway Dominique could see the shimmering lights below them. Long golden curtains hung at the windows also, and several lamps in a very contemporary design provided oases of brilliance. And yet in spite of its opulence Dominique thought it was a very attractive room, and one in which one could completely relax. Up here, away from the noise and bustle of the street, it was like being in the air-conditioned cabin of an airliner.

Then she became conscious of Vincente Santos again, as he closed the door and walked ahead of her down the steps and into the room.

'Well?' he said, somewhat mockingly. 'What do you think?'

Dominique stiffened. 'It's beautiful, of course. But you

32

don't need me to tell you that.'

'Agreed. However, I would like your honest opinion.'

'That is my honest opinion. Can we go now?'

'*Madre de Dios!*' he swore angrily. 'Relax, damn you! I'm not a monster. This is my apartment.'

'I gathered that.' Dominique hovered by the door.

'Then come and sit down.'

'I'd rather not.'

'Why not?'

'If – if John knew I was here – well – obviously he wouldn't like it.'

Vincente stared at her incredulously, and then he burst out laughing. 'Oh, God!' he exclaimed, at last. 'You knew your inestimable fiancé would not care for you to spend an evening in my company long before you left the hotel, didn't you?'

Dominique flushed. 'So?'

'So you took that risk and here you are!'

'What do you mean?'

Vincente loosened his tie and pulled it off. 'What do you think I mean?'

'I warn you, Mr. Santos, my fiancé—' she began hastily, glancing round at the door.

'Oh, grow up!' he muttered in disgust. 'Contrary to your beliefs, I do not attempt to seduce every female that comes within my orbit.'

'Then why have you brought me here?'

He shrugged. 'To talk to you.'

Dominique looked sceptical. 'About what?'

'You.' He removed his jacket. 'Come and sit down. It's hot, and you must be feeling the heat. Come on. Take it easy. Play it as it comes. Stop trying to anticipate something that may never happen.'

Dominique heaved a sigh. Obviously the whole of this

floor was leased by him. What chance would she have if he decided to take advantage of her? He had sent the lift away. She would not have time to summon it as a means of escape. She might as well accept that for the moment she had been foolish enough to place herself within his power.

As though aware of what thoughts were passing through her mind he said: 'No, you can't escape, so you might as well enjoy it. Come and sit down. I'll make you a drink.'

Dominique ventured down the steps and seated herself in one of the armchairs with the leopardskin seats. They were superbly comfortable, and she wriggled back comfortably, wishing she could kick off her shoes and relax completely. But that would have been like betraying herself, and she had no intention of doing that.

He handed her a drink, flung himself into a chair opposite and offered her a cigarette. When they were both lighted, he said:

'There, it's not so bad, is it?'

'Why have you brought me here, Mr. Santos?'

'Make it Vincente,' he said easily. 'Mr. Santos sounds ridiculous when you consider our situation. And your name is Dominique. I like it. It suits you.'

The way he said it, with a faintly foreign inflection, made it sound different from the way she had heard it before, and she liked it.

'Tell me, Mr. Santos,' she said, ignoring his edict, 'why did you come back to the hotel tonight?'

'I was curious.'

'About me?'

'Hmm. You intrigued me. You're frankly not the sort of woman I would have thought would find a man like Harding attractive.'

Dominique was staggered. He made outrageous remarks sound so ordinary.

34

'You don't know anything about me,' she exclaimed annoyedly.

'Don't I?' He drew on his cigarette lazily. 'I know you are what Sophia said you are – young and unsophisticated. Such a combination is a novelty to me. The women of my acquaintance acquire knowledge at a very early age.'

'Don't you mean experience?' asked Dominique tautly.

He shrugged. 'If you like,' he agreed equably.

He swallowed the remainder of his drink and left his seat to get another. As he did so, Dominique's eyes were drawn to a photograph on the low table nearby. It was the picture of a girl of perhaps nineteen or twenty. She was very attractive with short black curly hair and a small heart-shaped face. She wondered who it was a photograph of. Certainly it bore no resemblance to the woman Sophia.

He turned from the cocktail cabinet and intercepted her interest. 'And what thoughts are penetrating your devious little mind now?' he asked, a little harshly. 'That is my sister!'

'Oh!' Dominique took a sip of her drink. 'She's quite beautiful.'

'Yes, isn't she?' His mouth twisted sardonically. 'Beautiful – but unhappy.'

'Unhappy?' Dominique looked up.

'That is perhaps too weak an expression,' he said bleakly. 'Devastated is maybe nearer the truth.'

'But why?' Unwillingly, Dominique was curious.

'She fell in love with a man who was merely playing with her emotions,' replied Vincente grimly. 'When she discovered his true character she was distraught. She refused all offers of sympathy, and has locked herself away in the convent of St. Teresa.'

'I see.' Dominique stood down her glass. 'I'm sorry.'

35

He studied her thoughtfully. 'Are you? Are you, Dominique?'

Dominique ignored his penetrating gaze with difficulty. She glanced at her watch. 'Heavens! It's after one,' she exclaimed. 'I must go!'

'After one,' he mimicked her lazily. 'So late! You are tired?'

'Of course.' Dominique stood up.

'There are plenty of beds here,' he remarked mockingly.

Dominique turned a little pale. 'Please, Mr. Santos! Don't tease me!'

Vincente Santos stood down his own glass and came round to her side. 'Did I sound as though I was teasing?' he asked huskily.

Dominique stood her ground. 'I chose to take it that way,' she said, her own voice rather small and insignificant.

He hesitated, still looking at her, and then with an angry exclamation he turned and lifted his jacket. 'All right, all right, we go,' he said abruptly, and mounted the shallow steps in a single stride.

Dominique heaved a shaky sigh of relief and followed him.

Outside the air was deliciously cool, and she climbed into the car with trembling legs. Suddenly she felt very tired, as though the last half hour in Vincente's apartment had reduced her stamina to nil.

It seemed only seconds before they were drawing up outside the Hotel Maria Magdalena, and Vincente thrust open her door and indicated that she should get out. Obviously now he was eager to be rid of her.

She got out unsteadily, but he did not wait to see her into the hotel. As she mounted the steps the car roared away into the night.

In her room she stripped off her outer garments and then flung herself on the bed, aware of a sense of anti-climax. All of a sudden the evening had gone sour on her. She wasn't really sure why. It could be because of his easy acceptance of her resistance, but mainly she thought it was because to him the night was still young, and there would be other women, just like Sophia, eager and willing to satisfy his desires. But that was nothing to do with her. If he had attempted to make love to her she would have been horrified.

Or would she?

As she rolled miserably on to her stomach she acknowledged the plain fact that she would have liked to have known what it was like to have him touch her, caress her, and to feel that hard, cruel mouth exploring her own.

CHAPTER THREE

DESPITE her disturbed frame of mind Dominique slept well and was awakened by the sound of the traffic at about eight o'clock. It was a glorious morning, a shroud of mist enveloping the upper slopes of the city that presaged another hot day.

She showered and dressed in the cotton shift she had worn the previous afternoon, hoping it did not look too crumpled, but it was all she had apart from the navy dress and somehow she didn't want to wear it again just now. She applied make-up, did her hair, and went down to the restaurant a little before nine. She ate lemon flapjacks, drank several cups of coffee, and had the first and most enjoyable cigarette of the day.

At nine-forty-five she went back to her room, collected her things together, and carried her case down to the foyer. Then she seated herself on a red banquette to wait. However, after only a few moments the receptionist approached her.

'Ah, good morning, Miss Mallory,' he said. 'There is a car waiting for you outside. Will you go out?'

Dominique hesitated. 'My bill . . .' she began.

'That has all been taken care of,' replied the receptionist smoothly. 'I hope you complete your journey in safety.'

'Thank you. I've been very comfortable here. Good-bye.'

Frowning a little, she emerged from the swing doors on to the steps of the hotel. A dark saloon was waiting at the foot of the steps. As she appeared a man in chauffeur's uniform got out, and held open the rear door for her.

'Is – is this Mr. Santos's car?' she asked puzzled.

'*Sim, senhorita.*' The chauffeur nodded politely.

Dominique gave a faint sigh, and moved down the steps to climb into the back of the limousine.

'Where is Mr. Santos?' she asked· as casually as she could.

The chauffeur got into his place behind the wheel. 'Senhor Santos offers you his apologies, *senhorita*, but he has some urgent business to attend to. He has asked me to escort you to Bela Vista.'

Dominique's nails bit into the palms of her hands. 'I see.'

The vehicle moved smoothly away from the kerb, and she sank back against the soft upholstery. She felt disturbed and confused. Why had he decided not to take her after all? Was it something to do with what had happened last night? But what had happened, after all?

She lit another cigarette to calm her nerves. Forget Vincente Santos, she advised herself angrily. In an hour or so she would be with John. It was John she had come here to be with, not Vincente Santos.

The chauffeur drove more carefully than his employer, yet even so they reached the small domestic airport quite quickly. Dominique was ushered ceremoniously out of the limousine and into the gleaming silver and blue helicopter that awaited them. The chauffeur left the car in the hands of one of the airport stewards, and then shedding his peaked cap he climbed behind the controls of the aircraft. Dominique glanced at him. He was a man in his middle forties, she estimated, with dark skin and rather friendly blue eyes.

The propellers began to revolve, and in a few moments they were airborne. Dominique had never flown in a helicopter before and for a while she was terribly nervous. The panoramic window at the front gave one the impression that one was about to tip forward into oblivion, but after a minute or so she realized she was quite safe and began to enjoy it. Even so, it was quite a nerve-racking experience flying across such a bleak and savage landscape. The sawtooth peaks of the Serras seemed to beckon like devilish symbols, luring a man to destruction.

'What is your name?' she asked the man presently as she began to relax.

He gave her a smile. 'Salvador, *senhorita*,' he replied.

'And you work for Mr. Santos?'

'*Sim, senhorita*.'

Dominique nodded. 'You have known him long?'

'Twenty years, *senhorita*. Senhor Santos was only a boy when I came to work for him.'

This was interesting, and although she realized she ought not to feel so curious about Vincente Santos this was a way of learning a little more about him – about the enigma.

She was seeking about in her mind for a way of questioning Salvador without his actually being aware of it, when he said:

'You have come to Brazil to marry Senhor Harding, haven't you, *senhorita*?'

Dominique felt the hot colour surge into her cheeks, 'Yes,' she said shortly. 'Yes, I have.'

Salvador nodded, in a satisfied way, and Dominique had the impression he believed he had achieved something. Like master, like servant, she thought a trifle irritatedly.

But he had succeeded in halting further questions from his passenger. She realized that whatever she might ask now would merely make her sound unnecessarily curious.

'Does the journey take long?' she asked, assuming a cool indifference.

'Forty – maybe fifty minutes,' replied Salvador. 'You are

40

eager to reach your destination, *senhorita?*'

'Of course,' said Dominique briefly. Then: 'Do you know my fiancé?'

'Senhor Harding? Yes, *senhorita,* I know him.' Salvador was certainly not expansive in his answers to her questions.

Dominique sighed. Then she drew out her cigarettes. She seemed to be smoking far too much, but she needed something to do to fill in the time. When her cigarette was lit, Salvador said:

'What do you know of Bela Vista, *senhorita?*'

Dominique glanced at him. 'What do you mean?'

'Nothing of any consequence, *senhorita.* It is a beautiful little town. Set among these mountains like – how would you say – a rose among thorns. There are many blocks of new apartments, built by the government for the workers, and there are parks and places of interest. I am sure you will like living there.'

Dominique listened with interest. 'Do you live in Bela Vista, Salvador?'

'I live where Senhor Santos lives,' he replied simply. 'Sometimes at Bela Vista, sometimes in Rio, sometimes in Europe. Senhor Santos is a restless man, *senhorita.*'

'That I can believe,' remarked Dominique, a trifle dryly.

'It was not always so,' said Salvador, as though forced to give some explanation. 'But Senhor Santos is not a man to be easily understood. I can remember when he was a boy of perhaps fifteen or sixteen – eager for life – for experience. Now he has learned it is not experiences that destroy a man but people!'

Dominique studied the glowing tip of her cigarette. 'You're very loyal, Salvador,' she said curiously.

'Senhor Santos has given me everything,' said Salvador

fiercely. 'Education, occupation, position! I do not forget, *senhorita*.'

Dominique raised her dark eyebrows. Obviously Salvador considered Vincente Santos more than merely his employer. Then she gave her attention to the scenery. She was spending far too much time brooding on affairs that should be of no concern to her.

The hills in the morning light were a mixture of shades of grey and blue and brown, sometimes dark and forbidding, and at others green with foliage. In the ravines fast rivers surged unceasingly, while here and there were collections of dwellings, and the upward drift of blue smoke. A road wound between the hills like a dun-coloured snake, disappearing sometimes beneath the overhanging cliffs of hard rock. The shadow of the helicopter moved steadily onwards, and she began to wonder how much longer it would take. Then, suddenly, Salvador began the downward sweep and below she saw a green valley, spreading out as their height decreased, totally at variance with its surroundings. And in the valley she saw the town of Bela Vista.

There were houses on the outskirts of the town, huge affairs with swimming pools and tennis courts, while nearer the city were tall blocks of apartments, and offices, and schools. At the furthest point from the town towered a cluster of machinery and buildings that Dominique presumed must be the refinery and the laboratory where John worked.

The helicopter came down lower and below them Dominique could see a kind of park with a stretch of greenery big enough to take the powerful propellers of the helicopter. Salvador brought the craft level, steadied it, and then put it down neatly on the stretch of green, not far from the bustling main thoroughfare of Bela Vista.

'So we are here!' he said, giving her a slight smile. 'We

42

have landed safely, and there is your fiancé eagerly waiting for you.'

Dominique looked, saw several people at the perimeter of the area, all seeming strange and unfamiliar to her, and for a moment her heart missed a beat. Then she recognized John, but he had changed enormously. He now sported a thick beard and moustache, and his hair had grown rather long since his arrival. He must have had it cut, she supposed, but it was still straggling on the collar of his shirt. Big and broad, dressed in denim slacks and a brilliant orange shirt, he looked almost a stranger.

She got out of the helicopter carefully, with Salvador's assistance, and then before she had time to hesitate John was beside her, hugging her enthusiastically, pressing his rough cheeks to hers.

'Dominique, Dominique, Dominique,' he was saying excitedly. 'Oh, it's marvellous to see you, Dominique!'

She struggled to free herself, self-consciously aware of the eyes of the sightseers watching them. Salvador was watching them, too, a strange expression on his face.

'John!' she protested, at last. 'Let me get my breath!'

John gave her a final hug and then, keeping his arm across her shoulders, walked with her across to Salvador.

'Thanks, Salvador,' he said casually. 'Sorry about the mess-up! But these things happen, don't they?'

'It was nothing, *senhor*,' replied Salvador carefully.

Dominique noticed that his voice was cold. Obviously, like his master, he didn't like John much either.

Then they were free to go, and John was leading her across to a low slung blue car and putting her case into the back.

'Well?' he said, spreading his hands. 'What do you think of it?'

Dominique shook her head. She was not yet over her first

impressions of John, and his question made her aware of how engrossed she had been with her own feelings to the exclusion of everything else.

'I – I haven't had a chance to take much in yet,' she exclaimed. 'But from the air it was beautiful. It's amazing to think that such a place could flourish here, among these mountains.'

'Yes, isn't it? Still, you'll soon get used to it. I've been offered a permanent post here and I'm seriously thinking of accepting it.'

Dominique gave him a faint smile. 'Are you? I thought you only expected to be here about two years.'

'So I did,' replied John, turning on the ignition, and starting the engine. 'But like I said, they've offered me a better position, and I like it here now I've got used to it. Oh, I know it's a bit isolated, and some people don't like the country, but I do. And I'd like to see a lot more of it. I thought we'd take the opportunity on our honeymoon of exploring a bit of the interior. We can hire almost everything we need – tents, sleeping bags, cooking equipment and so on.'

Dominique wrinkled her nose. 'I thought we were going to Petropolis.'

'We were. But this is more exciting, don't you think?'

'I don't know,' said Dominique doubtfully, and it was left at that.

They drove along the Rua Carioca towards the outskirts of the city, and Dominique said: 'Where is your apartment?'

'Not far from here. But we're not going there. The Rawlings have a house, just outside of town, and they've invited us both for lunch. That's who you are staying with, you remember?'

'Of course.' Dominique nodded, quelling the feeling of

disappointment she felt that she was not to have some time alone with John for a while yet. There were so many things they needed to talk about, and she felt she needed to get to know him all over again. He seemed much different from the well-dressed, gentle young man she had known in England, and it was a little disturbing to realize you were going to marry someone in five weeks who had become a stranger to you. Still, she argued with herself, they would soon change that once they were alone together.

The Rawlings' house was detached but unobtrusive, without any of the expensive embellishments she had noticed on some of the houses here from the air. Inside, it was dull and unimaginative, and after meeting Marion Rawlings Dominique didn't have to wonder why.

Marion Rawlings was a woman of about thirty-five, with wheat-coloured hair that could have looked very attractive but didn't. She wore very old-fashioned dresses, which fell well below her knees, making Dominique supremely conscious of the shortness of her own skirt which had not seemed at all daring back in London, or Rio either for that matter.

She greeted Dominique with a lack of enthusiasm that was rather daunting, but her husband, Harry, more than made up for it, shaking hands with Dominique vigorously, while his rather narrow-spaced eyes viewed the attractive picture she made with a rather embarrassing intensity. Dominique decided she was not going to find the five weeks before her wedding passing very quickly.

The Rawlings had three children, all in their teens, a girl of thirteen, one of fourteen, and a boy of sixteen. They were friendly enough, asking questions about London, and generally making Dominique relax.

Lunch was salad and cold meat. The lettuce was soft and unappetizing, and the meat was still warm, much to Dominique's distaste. However, the fresh fruit that followed was delicious, as was the Brazilian coffee.

Talk became general, and Marion Rawlings said to Dominique: 'Do you think you're going to like it out here?'

Dominique smiled. 'I hope so,' she said, accepting a cigarette from John. 'I think it's a very exciting country, don't you?'

Marion Rawlings gasped, 'My dear girl, I've been here seven years, and I hate it. The heat, the flies, the insects at night. It's appalling! When John told us you were coming out here to marry him, well, quite frankly, I thought you were mad!'

Harry Rawlings gave a snort. 'Now, now, Marion, don't go giving the girl a bad impression of the place. You don't like it because there are no decent shops, and you can't get your hair done every few minutes. If you had something to occupy your time – like Alice Latimer, for example—'

'If you think I'm going into those filthy slums looking after even filthier children you're mistaken!' exclaimed Marion loudly. 'I've got better things to do with my time.'

'Like what?' asked Harry belligerently.

'Sewing, knitting, reading . . .'

'Huh!' Harry Rawlings sounded sceptical. 'It seems to me you spend far too much time sitting about the place gossiping with your old cronies. You and that Pedlar woman! You don't give anyone a moment's peace!'

'Don't you criticize me, Harry Rawlings!' she snapped angrily, and John glanced apologetically at Dominique.

'I really think we'll have to go,' he said, getting to his feet. 'I want to show Dominique the apartment, and naturally we have things to talk about.'

'I'll bet,' jeered Harry Rawlings, rather objectionably, and Dominique rose gladly, eager to make her escape.

Once in the car, and on their way back into town, she

said: 'Honestly, John, were they the only people you could ask to have me stay with?'

'Well, old Harry offered, and I didn't like to refuse,' explained John uncomfortably. 'I know Marion's a bit of a nag, but she does have a lot to put up with. Harry's no angel, and she has a pretty miserable life.'

'Oh, well, I suppose five weeks isn't long,' said Dominique dejectedly, and wondered why she should feel such a weight of depression over such a small thing. After all, she was here, wasn't she? She was with John again! What more did she want?

The apartment where John lived was, as he had said, spacious. It was bright and airy, and Dominique thought she could do a lot with it.

'Marion said you can use her sewing machine for curtains and covers and so on,' said John studying Dominique's reactions. Then: 'You're not sorry you came, are you, Dom?'

Dominique looked at his anxious face and suddenly ran into his arms. 'Oh, no, no, of course not,' she cried, hugging him, letting no other thoughts disturb her mind.

In the days that followed she became completely acclimatized. Actually, in the mountains the heat was not so intense and she didn't mind it at all. Her skin soon toned a honey colour, and her hair seemed a shade lighter. She filled her days working at the apartment. There was a lot she wanted to do. She got John to get her some paint and set about designing her own colour schemes. Then she went shopping and bought some material in the supermarket to make cushion covers and curtains to match. John had only acquired a table and some stools for the dining-room, and she decided to wait and see how their finances stood after the wedding and the honeymoon before spending extravagantly. There was a double bed in the main bedroom which John used at present, and a couple of lounge chairs. Altogether, he had adequate possessions, and had left Dominique plenty of opportunities to exercise her own prerogative.

At the Rawlings' she slept and ate breakfast, but for most of the day she was out of their house. Not that Marion wasn't friendly towards her, she was, but Dominique had the feeling that she and John would provide just another subject for discussion between Marion and her cronies.

Dominique had met the three women with whom Marion spent most of her time, and had not been impressed. They were all of an age and disposition, only living through the lives of their neighbours who lived, from their biased point of view, a thoroughly immoral existence. Dominique couldn't understand their reasoning. Couldn't they see that the world was going on its way and leaving them behind?

She and John resumed their relationship. It took a while, of course, and Dominique felt it was all her fault. But since John left England she had grown used to making decisions for herself and was not quite so willing to allow him to dominate her as he had used to do just after her father died. But she enjoyed working in the apartment, and in the evenings, when John came home and she cooked their evening meal, she could almost imagine they were married already. Not that John made any attempts to anticipate their married state, respecting her desire to keep their relationship warmly affectionate, and thus avoid any strain which might have developed in other circumstances.

The Santos Corporation provided recreational facilities for its staff, among them a golf and tennis club, and in the evenings sometimes John took Dominique down to the clubhouse where they sat beside the swimming pool and drank long cooling lagers and talked to his colleagues and their wives. As well as Harry Rawlings and Marion, Dominique got to know several other couples, although Marion's close friends did not appeal to her.

She had been in Bela Vista ten days when Vincente Santos's name cropped up again.

Since her arrival she had deliberately refrained from discussing him with John as she had sensed John's withdrawal on the subject, and it was from Marion and her cronies that she heard Vincente's name.

It was one morning when she was at the Rawlings' home, running up some curtains on Marion's sewing machine. Lynn Matthews, Susan Wheeler and Mary Pedlar were there, having coffee with Marion, and Dominique just happened to be sewing in the same room. It was Mary Pedlar who mentioned him first.

'I see Santos is back,' she remarked conspiratorially, glancing in Dominique's direction. 'Bob was talking to him yesterday at the plant.'

'Is he?' It was Marion who answered her. 'I didn't know that. I wonder how long he's staying this time. Is he alone?'

'I've no idea,' said Mary, shaking her head. 'Bob did say something about a board meeting being held in a couple of days. I expect he's here for that.'

'Most likely,' agreed Susan Wheeler. 'Have you met our chairman, Dominique?'

Dominique glanced up, pretending not to have listened to their conversation. 'What?' she asked. 'Your chairman? Who's that?'

Marion clucked her tongue. 'Of course she's met him,' she exclaimed. 'Heavens, didn't he meet her at the airport?'

Dominique's face suffused with the revealing colour she despised so much. 'You mean Mr. Santos?' she asked.

'Of course.'

'But how come Santos met John's fiancée?' exclaimed Lynn Matthews in astonishment. 'Heavens, I would have thought. . . .' Her voice tailed away at a look from Marion, and she added defensively: 'Well, I mean, he is the chairman, isn't he?'

Marion licked her lips in preparation for relating the story. 'There was a landslide, don't you remember?' she said, leaning forward. 'John phoned in to the refinery in the hope that there might be one of the staff in Rio who could be contacted to meet Dominique. Anyway, as it happened it was at a time when there were few people about and the call was directed to Santos's office by mistake. He happened to be on his way to Rio on business and he offered to meet Dominique there. After all, it was the reasonable thing to do. The girl couldn't be left stranded at Galeao, now could she?'

'No, but even so. . . .' Lynn sounded amazed.

'I know, but Santos does these unpredictable things sometimes, doesn't he?'

They all agreed, and Dominique concentrated on her sewing hoping that was the end of it. But of course it was not.

'Er – what did you think of him anyway, Dominique?' asked Marion, satisfying her curiosity at long last. 'I mean – he did escort you to your hotel, didn't he? It wasn't Salvador who met you, was it?'

Dominique smoothed the material under the needle. 'No,' she agreed. 'It was Mr. Santos who met me.'

'Well?' They were all eager for gossip, but Dominique felt a sense of distaste looking at their avid faces.

'He was very polite,' she replied carefully. 'What else is there?'

Marion looked annoyed, as though cheated of something she considered her right. Then she sniffed.

'They say he has a fabulous apartment in Rio,' she remarked, returning her attention to her friends. 'I've even heard that he has a different woman there living with him every month.'

Dominique stared at Marion, opened her mouth as though to speak, and then closed it again. No! She would not enter into such a discussion.

Marion looked back at Dominique. 'He has quite a reputation, you know,' she said conversationally. 'He's quite a playboy.'

Dominique grew irritated. 'Why are you telling me all this?' she asked pointedly.

Marion looked taken aback. 'No reason, of course. It's just that naturally we're concerned for your welfare!'

'My welfare? What has Vincente Santos to do with my welfare?'

The four women looked at one another knowingly, and Dominique could have kicked herself for using his Christian name as well as his surname. To their perverted minds it would escalate into something important.

'Well, dear,' said Susan, with a wry smile, 'you're rather attractive, and after all. . . .' Her voice trailed away.

Dominique got to her feet. 'Do you mind if I finish this later, Marion?' she asked.

Marion shrugged. 'Suit yourself, of course.'

'Thank you.'

Dominique walked swiftly out of the room, and closed the door with a definite click. Then she breathed a deep breath. Those women! She felt absolutely infuriated by their sick curiosity. Had they nothing better to do than indulge in this kind of gossip, inventing their own rumours if none existed?

She walked outside the building and seated herself on the veranda, under the shade of the trellised roof. Then she lit a cigarette and allowed her mind to drift, knowing full well that she would be the subject of their gossiping at this moment.

Even so, their news that Vincente Santos was in Bela Vista disturbed her a little. Was it possible that she might meet him, and if so what would she say to him? If only she had not agreed to spend that evening with him she would not have felt this sense of apprehension at meeting him again, mixed with a sense of guilt at her deception of John.

She glanced at her watch. It was a little after eleven. John was coming back for lunch to pick her up and take her into town to the apartment, but that would not be until nearly one. Whatever was she to do till then? She couldn't go back into the house. She had no desire to join Marion and her friends, even though she had left her coffee untouched and she would have liked a drink

Going into her bedroom, she collected her dark glasses, and changing her dress for cotton pants and a sleeveless blouse, and her shoes for thonged sandals, she left the house, and began to walk away from the town, towards the hills.

It was not too hot, and a faint breeze fanned her hot cheeks. Only her hair seemed a heavy weight on her shoulders, and she wondered whether she ought to have it cut. It would certainly be cooler and easier to handle.

She sighed and looked about her with interest. She was gradually climbing upwards, and when she looked back the Rawlings' house and its neighbours were some distance below her. The road forked at this point, one road leading higher into the mountains, and the other leading down towards the valley again, with the river in the distance.

She decided to take the latter road, and was glad when the going became less arduous as she began the descent. Here the road was lined with thick plantation growth and foliage, and shaded by huge trunks of trees. It was quieter here and although Dominique liked it she couldn't help but recall that Brazil was the country of the deadly rattlesnake, and that a quiet dusty road like this could be its natural habitat.

Because of this she quickened her step and when the road opened out again she was looking down on a part of the valley she had seen from the air but never from the ground. Here were the larger houses of the community, surrounded by high walls overhung by liana creeper and bougainvillea.

Sighing, she halted. This then would be where Vincente Santos lived, in one of these palatial dwellings. There were not very many, but what there were were very impressive. She turned back at this point. She had no desire to meet Santos himself when her thoughts were already disturbed by Marion's words.

She plodded back up the incline, and reached the belt of trees. When she heard the sound of a car's engine, she almost jumped out of her skin. She had been listening for noises in the undergrowth, and so concentrated had been her involvement that she found it difficult to distinguish what the sound was at first.

Thus she was standing with her hands pressed to her lips when the car swung round the curve and halted abruptly beside her.

'Hello,' said a lazy voice, and the colour returned to her face.

'Vin— I mean – *you!*' she exclaimed.

He smiled and slid out of the car. Dressed in close-fitting cream pants and a cream silk sweater which was unbuttoned almost to his waist revealing the dark mass of hairs on his broad chest he looked lithe and masculine, and she bent her head, unwilling to appear glad to see him.

He put a hand under her chin, and forced her head up,

however. 'Well?' he said. 'It was to have been Vincente, wasn't it?' Then he leaned back against the bonnet of the car. 'Where have you been? I've been looking for you.'

'You – you've been looking for me!' she gasped. 'You – you haven't been to the Rawlings?'

'Why not? Marion told me that you must have gone for a walk. How else would I have found you so easily?'

'Oh, lord!' exclaimed Dominique, staring at him in exasperation. 'Why on earth did you do that? What do you want to see me for?'

'I'm beginning to wonder,' he remarked, a trifle dryly.

'Well!' Dominique moved restlessly. 'You've lived here, You must know what kind of woman Marion Rawlings is! Heavens, I'll be branded as a scarlet woman by merely speaking to you!' She bit her lip.

Vincente Santos's hand gripped the rim of the car's bonnet for a moment, and then he said tautly: 'And that bothers you? Why? Because of Harding?'

Dominique sighed. 'Why did you come?'

'Because I wanted to,' he replied harshly. 'Get in the car. I want to talk to you.'

Dominique hesitated, and then as once before she gave in. He slid in beside her and turned towards her, his arm along the back of her seat, his fingers playing with the tendrils of her hair. 'Well?' he murmured questioningly, 'is it love's young dream?'

Dominique was unable to relax. 'What do you mean?'

'Now you're pretending you don't know,' he said softly. 'I mean Harding, of course.'

'That's nothing to do with you,' she said stiffly.

'Of course it is. I want you to be happy.'

Dominique looked at him out of the corners of her eyes. 'Why should my feelings interest you?' she asked unevenly.

His eyes were slightly narrowed against the glare of the sun, and she noticed how long and thick were his lashes. With his free hand he lifted the dark glasses from her nose and threw them on the parcel shelf.

'Don't you know the answer to that either?' he murmured lazily.

'No! No, of course not!' Dominique was swift to answer him.

He lifted a handful of her hair and wound it round his fingers and then drew her towards him, slowly and persistently. 'Your hair is beautiful,' he said huskily.

'Please,' she began unsteadily. 'I – I must get back.'

'Must you?'

His fingers slid her blouse from one creamy shoulder and then she felt the warmth of his mouth caressing her skin. Her whole body seemed to be a mass of unfamiliar emotions, most persistent of all was a desire for him to go on caressing her.

'Vincente,' she murmured achingly. 'This is crazy!' Her breath was swift and uneven.

'Yes, isn't it?' he muttered, caressing her bare arm with his hard fingers while his mouth sought the nape of her neck. 'You smell divine, Dominique, put your arms round my neck.'

'No,' she said, managing to turn her face away by a great effort of will power.

'Yes,' he commanded a trifle thickly, and with hard deliberate hands he pressed her mouth to his, his fingers in the silky mass of her hair. She tried to push him away, but her hands came up against the hard strength of his bare chest and seemed unwilling to obey the dictates of her brain. Instead, they slid round his neck, drawing him even closer, and she found herself clinging to him, allowing the force of his passion to destroy all her inhibitions.

55

John had never kissed her in this way, so that she seemed to be drowning in feeling, sensual feeling. In fact she wasn't at all sure he was capable of doing so. There was something wholly primitive about Vincente Santos's emotions that seemed to penetrate her whole being, seducing her to complete submission.

Then, firmly, he put her away from him, and merely sat looking at her with lazy eyes as she confusedly fastened the buttons of her blouse and endeavoured to restore some order to her tousled hair.

'No, don't,' he said huskily. 'Leave it. I like it the way it is. You look very desirable. Come back to the house – my house – now.'

Dominique did not trust herself to speak. She merely shook her head wildly, aware that something terrible had happened and she must not allow it to continue.

'Dominique,' he said persuasively. 'Don't be afraid! You know you want to.'

'No,' she said jerkily. 'No, you're wrong!'

'Prove it,' he said, his voice harder now.

'How?' she looked at him with eyes that were still a trifle glazed from her emotions.

'Come and have lunch with me!'

She shook her head again. 'No. *No!*' Opening the car door she slid out and without another word she set off to run down the road towards the Rawlings' house. The heat was intense now and the unfamiliar exercise brought a film of sweat out all over her body, but she had to get away, and she knew he wouldn't allow her to do so without a struggle. The trouble was that the biggest struggle was taking place inside herself. She had wanted to go with him, he had been right!

Once she glanced back, but the car was still parked where she had left him. To turn he would have to make a good many moves, and she knew he would not take the trouble. He had no need. He thought that sooner or later she would give in.

What frightened her most was the realization that she thought so, too.

CHAPTER FOUR

DOMINIQUE slowed her steps before she reached the Rawlings' house, but even so, she felt hot and uncomfortable, a feeling that was heightened when she recognized John sitting on the veranda with Harry and Marion, drinking lager and smoking cigarettes. She wondered desperately whether Marion had made any insinuative remarks concerning herself and Vincente Santos, and it was difficult to appear casual with so many disturbing thoughts on her mind.

'Enjoy your walk?' asked Marion silkily, observing Dominique with her usual intensity.

'Thank you, yes. Hello, John, you're early!' She managed to give a faint smile that included Harry. 'Gosh, it's hot now!'

'Have you been running, Dominique?' asked John, in surprise. 'You needn't have done. You're not late.'

Dominique seized this remark, and said: 'I wasn't sure what time it was, and I wanted to get changed before you arrived.'

Marion tapped ash from her cigarette into the ashtray. 'Er – did you see Mr. Santos?' she asked casually.

John looked questioningly at her. 'Why should Dominique see Santos?' he asked.

Marion shrugged her thin shoulders. 'Well, he called here, soon after she had left. I believe he wanted to assure himself that Salvador had delivered her safely.' She smiled rather mockingly.

John looked at Dominique. 'Well?' he said. 'Did you see him?'

Dominique stiffened her shoulders. 'Yes, I saw him.'

58

'And?'

'And what? What's all the fuss about?' Dominique hid her nervousness in defiance.

'What did he say to you? I presume he did stop and speak to you.' John sounded furious.

'Yes, he stopped. He didn't say much at all. I expect as Marion said he wanted to assure himself that I had arrived safely.'

'Some chance!' muttered John angrily. 'Honestly, Dominique, I'll be the laughing stock of the plant if this leaks out!'

Dominique put her hands on her hips. 'If what leaks out?' she exclaimed, trembling inwardly, but outwardly appearing calm.

'Santos – coming here – looking for you! For God's sake, Dominique, why did you have to go walking today of all days? If you'd been here when he arrived it wouldn't have sounded so bad!'

Harry Rawlings interposed, 'Leave the girl alone, John! She hasn't done anything. It's not her fault that she's so damned attractive!'

Dominique felt her colour rising, and moved to the door of the house. 'Can I go and get changed, now?' she asked, with assumed nonchalance.

John shrugged. 'I suppose so. But keep away from him in future, Dominique.'

Dominique was about to protest that she had not sought Vincente Santos's company, and then decided not to bother. Already her conscience was troubling her, and she couldn't argue with John about something that still terrified her by its enormity.

However, when she emerged from the shower, she had managed to put all thoughts of Santos to the back of her mind, deliberately listening carefully to every remark John made, trying to fill her mind to the exclusion of everything else. John soon recovered his good spirits and there was only Marion's speculative glances to contend with. Harry Rawlings seemed to think nothing of it, although Dominique suspected this was because he himself was no innocent and he supported a policy of live and let live.

During the next few days Dominique devoted herself to her work at the apartment. She had redecorated the lounge, painting the walls a stark white and adding some hand-painted plaques she had brought with her from England and which looked wonderful against such a background.

She had explored the town quite fully now, and liked what she had seen, except for the slum areas which seemed to spring up wherever there were towns. The centre of the town was laid out with spacious avenues and parks marching side by side, and trees had been planted beside the fountains and lakes. The shops were not as comprehensive as they could have been and she did most of her shopping at a huge supermarket that supplied everything from reels of cotton to motor cars. There were few dress shops and what there were were very expensive. Their styles were not particularly modern either, and Dominique was glad she could use a sewing machine. Once she and John were married she intended to buy one and make her own clothes as she had sometimes done when she lived with her father.

It was an easy walk from the apartment to the centre of the town and as John used the car to get out to the refinery Dominique grew used to walking everywhere. In consequence her tan deepened and in her short swinging skirts which showed a delicious length of slender leg she attracted quite a lot of attention. She had got into the habit of plaiting her hair and winding it round her head. That way it kept tidy as well as keeping her cool.

At the end of her second week in Bela Vista John came

home one evening looking rather pensive.

Immediately Dominique felt apprehensive. She had not yet got over her encounter with Vincente Santos and she sensed that something had happened and prayed it was nothing to do with herself.

'What's wrong?' she asked lightly, as she served up a light omelette and salad, done in the way John liked it.

John flung himself into his chair and looked at her moodily. 'Nothing much, you might think,' he muttered broodingly. 'Here, what do you make of this?'

He flung a white envelope on the table. With trembling fingers Dominique opened it and withdrew the white card that was inside. It was an invitation – from Vincente Santos!

She looked up before reading it, conscious of John's eyes upon her. 'What is it?' she asked.

'Can't you read?' asked John sulkily. 'It's an invitation, what do you think? Mr. Vincente Santos requests the pleasure of the company of Mr. John Harding and his fiancée, Miss Dominique Mallory, at a dinner party to be held on Monday evening, etc, etc!'

Dominique glanced down, unable to meet John's eyes as her heart began to flutter rapidly. 'Oh, yes?' she said uncomfortably.

'Oh, yes!' John got to his feet and swung her round to face him. 'What does it mean, Dominique?'

Dominique felt the hot colour flood her cheeks. 'What do you mean? It's nothing to do with me!'

'Isn't it? Isn't it? It just so happens I've never been invited to a dinner party at the Santos residence before! That's what it means!'

Dominique felt slightly sick. 'And – and you think he's sent this because of me?'

'Well, hasn't he? What other reason can there be? Goddammit, Dominique, what is there between you two?'

Dominique swallowed hard. 'Between us!' she echoed. 'There – there's nothing between us. I – I scarcely know the man!' Oh, God, she thought inwardly, forgive me for all these lies! But what can I say?

John flung himself across the room, and poured himself a generous measure of whisky. He flung the drink to the back of his throat, and turned to look at her again. 'Well, this settles one thing,' he muttered. 'I shan't be taking any permanent posts here!'

'John,' she began unsteadily. 'We don't have to go. We can refuse!'

'Can we? Can we? Oh, Dominique, don't be naïve! We can't refuse. Vincente Santos is the chairman of the Santos Corporation!'

Dominique stared at him. 'But – but when I asked you whether he was your boss you said no!' she exclaimed.

'Well, it's true – in a way. Rivas does all the actual management. Santos works at the refinery as and when it suits him. Anyway, there are other plants about the country. He can't spend all his time in one place.'

'But why can't we refuse?'

'Oh, Dominique! Don't you realize? This is a *royal* summons! No one – but no one – refuses Santos's invitations!'

'Well, we will,' said Dominique firmly, going across to the cooker to make her own omelette. 'I'm not afraid of him!'

Yet even as she said the words she knew they were not true. She was afraid of him – or rather of the reaction he produced in herself!

John was looking a little more amiable. 'I would have thought you would be eager to go,' he muttered reluctantly.

Dominique sighed. 'Well, I'm not,' she said shortly.

'No, I can see that.' John snorted angrily. 'But we'll still have to go.' He shrugged. 'It may not be so bad. I've wanted to see inside his place for some time.'

Dominique stared at him. 'But we can't, John!' she exclaimed.

John looked at her curiously. 'Why not?'

Dominique gave an exasperated movement. 'A moment ago you were cursing because you had to go. Now you say we're going. Why? Why? Are you afraid of him?'

'No, but he is the big man, after all.'

Dominique turned away, not trusting herself to look at him. She felt sick and confused. They were going. Santos had known they would. Oh, why was he doing this? Deliberately setting out to torment her!

John seated himself at the table and attacked his meal with enthusiasm. 'I'm glad you're not impressed by him, Dom,' he said, his mouth full of egg and lettuce. 'I might have known you weren't like the other women! Hell, half of them would give their eye-teeth for the opportunity to see inside Minha Terra.'

Dominique lifted her omelette out of the pan, her appetite diminishing. However would she be able to get through an evening in Vincente Santos's presence, with John beside her, watching her every move?

On the day of the dinner party, which as John had expected had caused much speculation among his friends, Dominique spent some time examining the contents of her wardrobe. Her clothes were mostly informal. In England almost anything would do for evening wear and she had a couple of jersey slack suits which she might have considered in London but which would be bound to look out of place here. Eventually she decided on a black tunic, straight and

63

simple, with an overlying skirt of strands of gold lamé. It was rather way-out, she thought a little dryly, as she laid it on her bed in her room at the Rawlings', but at least it looked suitable. She had bought it in a boutique in London which she had visited with the girls from the adjoining flat to her own, and they had encouraged her to do so. Certainly it suited her, but would Vincente Santos think she had worn it for his benefit? And why did she want to look her best anyway?

But of course, she knew the answer to that!

There was a tap at her door, and without waiting for a reply, Marion entered, her eyes widening when she saw the black and gold dress.

'Well, well!' she said. 'Is that what you're going to wear tonight?'

Dominique stifled her annoyance. 'Yes. Do you think it's all right?'

Marion studied it thoughtfully. 'It's rather short, isn't it?' she asked critically, as Dominique held it against herself.

Dominique threw it back on the bed. 'So are all the clothes being worn in England at the moment,' she said. 'Oh, there are maxis and midis, and goodness knows what else, but I prefer the short lengths, myself.'

'So I've noticed,' remarked Marion, rather spitefully. 'However, John will no doubt change his mind about that once you're married.'

Dominique frowned. 'What do you mean?'

'Well, no man worth his salt wants his wife going around exhibiting herself for every other man to stare at,' returned Marion coolly. 'Men like Vincente Santos, for example.'

Dominique bit her lip. Marion was baiting her, she knew, and she would not allow her to get away with it.

'Did you want something, Marion?' she asked sweetly.

Marion shrugged. 'Nothing in particular. Just a chat,' she

replied, sitting on the end of Dominique's bed. 'Tell me, Dominique, what really happened that day Santos came here looking for you? Did you really know he was coming?'

Dominique turned away. 'Of course I didn't,' she said, controlling her temper with difficulty. 'And I told you what happened.'

'You told John what happened. But that's a different story, isn't it, Dominique? I mean, I don't believe that stuff about him being concerned for your welfare, and so on! That's not what he came for. I know Vincente Santos!'

Dominique swung round. 'That's just the point, *you don't*!' she retorted, forgetting for a moment to whom she was speaking. 'You know absolutely nothing about him! Only the gossip you can dig up about him!'

Marion looked flabbergasted. 'And you know everything about him, I suppose?' she sneered.

Dominique bent her head, recovering her composure. 'No. No, I didn't say that. I – I said you knew nothing. That's something else again.'

'But how come you can pass any opinion, either way?' snapped Marion. 'Unless you've had experience, of course!'

Dominique clenched her fists. 'Do you mind leaving my room, Marion?' she asked tightly. 'I – I want to wash my hair!'

Marion seemed about to say more, but then they both heard the children, coming in from school, calling to their mother. Marion gave Dominique a furious stare, and then she left, slamming the door behind her.

After she had gone, Dominique leant against the door weakly for a moment, wishing there was a key so that she could be certain of some privacy in future. Then she straightened, and walking through to the bathroom, began to wash her hair with lethargic movements. There was still over two weeks to go to her wedding. However were she and Marion to get along together until then?

In the afternoon, Dominique dried her hair thoroughly, and then combed it out ready to plait for the evening. She was in the process of doing her hair when she heard John arrive. She called: 'Hang on a minute, I'm nearly ready,' and hastily plaited the last bit and pinned it up. She had already done her make-up, and taking off her bathrobe she pulled on the black dress.

Then she studied her reflection in the mirror. She looked tall and slim and rather sophisticated, she thought, which was a change from her usual casual appearance. Pearl studs glinted in her ears, but she had left her throat bare. The dress had quite a high neckline and required no ornamentation.

John was wearing a dinner jacket for the first time since her arrival in Brazil, and looked big and broad and attractive. She thought his beard added distinction to his otherwise boyish features, and prayed she would be able to remain as cool as she felt at present.

'You look marvellous!' muttered John enthusiastically, when she appeared. 'Don't you think so, Harry?'

Harry Rawlings whistled. 'I'll say. Wish I was going myself. I wonder who else will be there?'

John shrugged. 'Well, Rivas and his wife for certain. I don't know who else.'

Harry nodded. 'Hmm, well, enjoy yourself, children. What do you say, Marion?'

Marion moved her shoulders indifferently. 'I wouldn't want to eat with that man,' she replied coldly. 'I'm particular who I associate with.'

'Chance would be a fine thing,' remarked Harry dryly, chuckling.

They drove away from the Rawlings' house in the direction of the town, and Dominique frowned. 'Where are we going?'

'To Minha Terra!' said John in surprise.

'Isn't it up there?' She pointed back up the darkened road where she had walked several days ago.

'What? Santos's house? It's not among the rank and file! No, you'll see. Just wait! It's a pity it's dark, that's all.'

They left the bright lights of the town on a road Dominique had not travelled before, curving up into the mountains where only the trees seemed to prevent the car from tipping off the hairpin track altogether. Even in the dark the view was quite spectacular as the lights grew smaller below them, but Dominique was too busy clinging to her seat to pay much attention to anything else.

Eventually they emerged on to a plateau, and Dominique gave a gasp of pleasure. There was the house, floodlit tonight, looking like a small white-painted fortress, with turrets and grilled windows, standing among a mass of trees and shrubs. There was quite a high wall all around the property, but the tall grilled gates stood wide and Dominique could see that there were already several cars parked on the forecourt.

John gave her a didn't-I-tell-you look, then drove between the gates into the courtyard. This area was bright with flowers and shrubs, looking strange and exotic in the artificial lights. There were plants in tubs, and trailing over trellises, while a stone cherub stood in the centre of a paved surround, continually spouting water from its mouth.

Dominique slid out of the car without waiting for John, and crossed to a low wall at the side of the courtyard that invited inspection. Then she stared in amazement, a thrill of pure excitement assailing her. Below her, the ground fell away sharply in a steep precipice, to the valley below, where

67

the lights of Bela Vista winked and glittered like fairy lights. John came to join her and voiced his own appreciation.

'Some place, isn't it?' he muttered, in a low voice. 'This is all private land, you know, the road, everything! Santos doesn't believe in anybody getting too familiar, unless he wants it that way, of course,' he added.

Dominique turned, and said: 'Do we go in?'

Her question was left unanswered, however, as Salvador appeared at that moment, dressed this evening in a dinner suit, its white jacket faultlessly pressed.

'Good evening, Miss Mallory,' he said politely. 'Mr. Harding.'

'Oh, hello there, Salvador,' said John, rather awkwardly. 'Will you tell Mr. Santos we're here?'

Dominique felt her stomach flutter uncomfortably. All of a sudden she wanted to turn and run, as she had run before. She wanted to escape from whatever it was that was compelling her to stay. But of course she remained calm, and when Salvador asked them to follow him, she did so, her legs obeying the dictates of her brain.

They crossed the terrace and entered the house through French doors into a long low lounge. Dominique registered that its decorations were coolly blue and green, and that there were some magnificent curtains at the windows, and then they emerged out of the house again. The lounge apparently ran from front to back, and it was here, on a wide paved patio, that Vincente Santos and his guests were taking pre-dinner drinks.

The patio was discreetly lit by coach lamps, and here was another magnificent view of the valley. To the right, Dominique could vaguely disinguish formal gardens, and a swimming pool which seemed to curve out of sight, overhung with flowering shrubs in places.

But the guests on the patio, lounging gracefully in comfortable chairs caught her immediate attention, and she was glad she had chosen to wear the black dress. There were more dramatic creations here.

Then Vincente Santos detached himself from a group of people and came to greet them. In a dark dinner suit, his linen immaculate, his thin face wearing a strange expression, Dominique thought he was easily the most interesting man there, even though some of the men were more handsome. His lean hard body made John look rather clumsy and over-fed, and she closed her eyes for a moment, willing these thoughts away.

Then he was saying: 'Good evening, Harding. I'm so glad you could come and bring your most charming fiancée.'

John seemed tongue-tied and youthful. 'Thank you for inviting us, *senhor*,' he said hastily. 'It's a beautiful place you have here!'

'Yes, beautiful,' agreed Vincente Santos sardonically, but he was not looking at the view, he was looking at Dominique. 'And how are you this evening, Miss Mallory? Well, I trust.'

'I – I'm fine, thank you, Mr. Santos,' replied Dominique, trying not to sound nervous.

Vincente Santos gave her a slight smile, and then said: 'Claudia, come here a moment. I want you to meet Mr. Harding and Miss Mallory.'

A girl came to join them. She was a redhead, her hair a riot of tawny curls. She was wearing a culotte suit of floral silk that shimmered as she moved. She was smaller than Dominique, and rather more voluptuously built.

'Yes, Vincente?' she murmured, looking up at him intimately.

'Claudia, show Mr. Harding around, would you? Introduce him to my other guests while I do the same for Miss Mallory.'

69

Dominique sensed John's disapproval, but there was nothing either of them could do about it. The girl Claudia was leading John away and she was left with Vincente Santos.

However, Vincente was not prepared to embarrass her yet awhile and taking her elbow in his fingers he guided her across to a group of people and began making introductions. Dominique estimated that there must be about twenty guests altogether, but their names became indistinguishable in her mind. She only recalled Frederick Rivas and his wife Alicia. And that was because she had already heard John mention her name. She accepted a Martini cocktail and a cigarette, and managed to make polite conversation with anyone who spoke to her. Vincente seemed quite content to remain in the background, watching her, watching the impression she made on his guests.

Certainly the male members of the party gravitated in her direction. Not only was she very atractive, but she had a keen sense of humour and could parry their comments quite naturally. Surprisingly, she did not feel out of her element as she had expected to do, and only John's glowering face, whenever she caught sight of him, warned her of his anger.

Dinner was announced, and they entered a long dining-room where a polished wood table had been laid with lace place mats and gleaming cutlery. Cut wine-glasses caught the light, throwing it back in prisms of colour, and as it was diffused the room had a very intimate atmosphere. A centre piece of scarlet poinsettia and creamy magnolias in the green leaves of a rubber plant was quite arresting, and overhead a huge fan disturbed the warm night air.

Dominique was seated on their host's left hand, with the girl Claudia on his right. John was seated further down the table, and as Dominique gave Vincente a startled glance at this arrangement she surprised a curiously triumphant look in his eyes. Then the look disappeared and he was the bland host again, exchanging pleasantries, discussing the merits of the wine they drank with the meal.

But Dominique barely noticed what she ate. She was overwhelmingly conscious that Vincente Santos had deliberately set out to separate her from John, and not only physically, and she felt a mixture of fury and frustration. Fury, because he had no right to attempt such a thing, and frustration, because in spite of everything, she was still attracted to him.

Claudia was captured in conversation by the young man on her right, and Vincente bent his head towards Dominique.

'You look very beautiful this evening,' he murmured softly. 'Was it all for Harding's benefit?'

Dominique compressed her lips for a moment. 'Why are you doing this?' she said, between her teeth.

'Doing what?' he asked, lifting his wine-glass to his lips, looking round urbanely as though they were discussing the weather.

Dominique's fingers were clenched. 'You *know*,' she said, her voice taut.

'Do I?' He smiled at her charmingly. 'Tell me!' His eyes taunted her.

Dominique refused to look at him, bending her head jerkily. 'I – I think you're despicable!' she exclaimed, in a low voice.

'No, you don't,' he replied smoothly.

'You know John is absolutely furious,' she said angrily. 'He already suspects that there was something behind this invitation!'

'So there was,' he replied lazily. 'Do you like this beef? My chef, Maurice, has a special way of preparing it.'

Dominique looked along the table at John and smiled appealingly, but John merely gave her a hard look and then concentrated on his food. She bit her lip, and looked at her own plate. Her nerves were jumping, and she wished she had drunk several glasses of some kind of spirit before attending the dinner party. That way at least she might have been able to enjoy it.

Vincente finished his course, and pushed his plate aside, resting his arm on the table, turned in Dominique's direction. 'Talk to me,' he said softly. 'I like listening to you.'

Dominique shook her head. 'For pity's sake,' she said tightly. 'Leave me alone!'

'You would really like me to do that?' he murmured questioningly.

'Isn't it obvious?'

'No. What is obvious is that I disturb you just as much as you disturb me!'

Dominique pushed her own unfinished plate aside. 'Your reputation hardly does you credit, *senhor*,' she said bitterly.

'And you believe everything you hear?'

'What do you mean?'

He shrugged. 'Let it pass!'

'I think you enjoy baiting me,' she said, twisting her fingers together.

'What would you rather I did?'

'I've told you. Leave me alone!'

'And if I did – you wouldn't object?'

Dominique stared at him. 'Of course not.'

He half-smiled. 'Do you know what I think? I think you would be jealous!'

'Jealous!' Dominique almost uttered the word loudly. 'You're crazy!'

72

'Am I?' He lay back in his chair. 'All right. We shall see.'

And thereafter for the remainder of the meal, he ignored her, much to her relief. Even so, though, she had to admit his company was stimulating, and the other men seemed dull in comparison.

Afterwards they all adjourned to the lounge which Dominique had seen on their arrival. The carpets had been cleared for dancing, and a record player gave off soft music, as well as the more energetic beat numbers. A buffet had been laid on the patio for anyone who was still hungry, and there was drink of every kind.

Dominique found John beside her, and he steered her on to the patio before they could be intercepted by anyone else.

'What's going on?' he asked, in a low angry voice. 'What was the idea of sitting with Santos at dinner?'

Dominique spread her hands expressively. 'John, I had no choice. I was put there, and you know it. Maybe your charming chairman likes to be surrounded by women.'

'That goes without saying,' muttered John furiously. 'God help me, Dominique, why did we come here?'

'Well, don't start that now!' she said, rather shortly. 'You were curious enough to see his house. Well, now you've seen it!'

'Yes, some place, isn't it!'

'You said that before.' Dominique glanced around, aware that people were watching them. 'Look, John, let's leave the post-mortem till later. And if we get separated again, just remember, there are only so many hours in every day. It can't last for ever!'

But even as she said these words, she realized that she was not as eager as he was to leave. There was a fatalistic kind of masochism in staying.

Dancing began, and John took Dominique back into the lounge to dance with her. Dominique looked around, unwillingly aware that she was looking for Vincente Santos.

Then she saw him. He was dancing with Claudia. Her arms were wrapped around his neck, and her body was moulded to his. They made a very attractive couple, Dominique had to admit, but something inside her seemed to be tearing her apart. She wouldn't – she *couldn't* be jealous! Yet she knew her feelings had some basis in that awful emotion.

'Let's have a drink,' she said brightly, drawing John back out to the patio. 'We'll sit on the patio and look at the view.'

John was amiable enough, and they sat together, talking about the improvements Dominique was making to the apartment. John got them both a drink, Dominique's was a brandy and soda, and they had cigarettes. The Rivases came to join them later.

'You look comfortable here,' remarked Frederick Rivas to Dominique. 'It is a wonderful house, is it not? And the view! Ah!' he sighed.

Dominique smiled. 'Yes, it is a fabulous place,' she agreed. 'I expect you've been here in daylight. Is it really as magnificent a view as one would imagine?'

'But yes!' Rivas nodded. 'One can see to the hills in every direction. Sometimes I think Vincente is like the eagle in his eyrie, no?'

Even John smiled at this, and conversation became more natural. Alicia Rivas was friendly, and not at all devious like Marion Rawlings, and Dominique liked her.

'Do you have any children, *senhora*?' Dominique asked.

'One only,' replied Alicia sadly. 'We wanted more, but it was not to be. Roderigo is fourteen now, and away at boarding school in the United States.'

'I expect you miss him,' said Dominique sympathetically.

74

'I do, of course,' nodded Alicia. 'But I fill my days quite easily. There is plenty to do in Bela Vista if one is energetic enough to do it. Do you swim, Miss Mallory?'

'Yes.'

'Then you must come and use our pool some time,' said Alicia firmly. 'I would enjoy your company, and we are soon to be neighbours, no?'

Dominique agreed enthusiastically, and they were still talking when Salvador appeared. 'Is Senhor Santos here?' he asked.

'No, Salvador,' replied Frederick Rivas. 'He was with Claudia. But they both seem to have disappeared!'

Salvador glanced at Dominique, and then nodded. '*Sim, senhor.*'

Salvador went back into the house, and Dominique drew on her cigarette deeply. Had Salvador done that on purpose? Had he deliberately drawn attention to the fact that both Vincente Santos and the girl had gone off together?

She felt her nerves jumping again. Where was Vincente now? Was he with Claudia? What part did she play in his life? Was she even at this moment in his arms somewhere?

Her relief when Vincente suddenly appeared in the doorway was almost overpowering. He walked across to their group lazily, having a word here and there with other guests he passed. Then he reached the group and looked down at them, his eyes lingering on Dominique, much to her confusion.

'Well, my friends,' he said. 'You are enjoying yourselves?'

Frederick Rivas smiled. 'But of course, Vincente. The meal was exquisite, as usual.'

'That is good. I am pleased.' Vincente stood on the stub of the cigarette he had been smoking. 'Miss Mallory, will you dance with me?'

Dominique glanced at John's suddenly set face. 'I – I'd rather not,' she stammered.

'But you must!' he exclaimed lazily. 'I am your host, and I command it.' He softened his words with a smile.

'You'd better agree,' remarked Alicia, smiling. 'Vincente can be very persuasive!'

Dominique hesitated only a moment, and then, as it was expected of her, she rose to her feet and allowed him to guide her into the lounge.

On the polished dance floor, almost deserted now as the guests sought refreshment of various kinds, he drew her close against him, imprisoning her with his arms close around her.

'This isn't the conventional way to dance,' she protested, as her hands rested against his chest.

'I am not a conventional man,' he replied lazily, allowing his lips to caress her hair. 'Oh, Dominique, you're adorable!'

'Vincente,' she murmured, not trying any longer to pretend to use his surname, 'John may be watching you.'

'You think I am afraid of your Mr. Harding?'

'No. But I am.'

'No, you are not. You are happy here, in my arms. You would like me to kiss you.' He bit her ear with his teeth momentarily.

Dominique felt as though her whole body was on fire. 'Don't,' she whispered pleadingly. 'Don't!'

He gave a lazy laugh. 'You are more willing now, though,' he murmured. 'You did not like to see me dancing with Claudia.'

Dominique gave him a haughty look. 'Your affairs have nothing to do with me,' she said angrily.

'They do, Dominique,' he persisted, allowing one hand to stray caressingly along the curve of her spine.

76

'How can you say that? When only a few minutes ago you must have been—' She broke off. 'You make me sick!'

'A few minutes ago – what?' he asked abruptly.

'You disappeared – and so did Claudia.'

'Ah!' he nodded. 'And you think I have been making love to Claudia?'

Dominique flushed. 'It's obvious, isn't it? You said you would try to make me jealous!'

He bent his head and kissed the curve of her neck. 'Claudia is over there – see? With José Bianca, my manager.'

Dominique twisted her neck away from his mouth. 'You didn't make love to her?'

'No. There is only one woman here I want to make love to,' he murmured huskily. 'Do you think I would take anyone else?'

Dominique's breathing was difficult. 'So you did invite us here because of the other morning,' she said unsteadily.

'Because of the other morning – yes and no. Yes, I wanted to see you again, but it began much sooner than the other morning. It began when I saw you at the airport.'

Dominique glanced round, saw they were alone. 'I – I've got to get back to John,' she protested unevenly.

Vincente loosened his hold on her to take her hand. 'Come with me,' he said. 'I want to talk to you – alone!'

'No. We mustn't!'

'*I* must,' he muttered rather huskily, and she did not resist.

He led her through an arched doorway into a wide hall, with a shallow marble staircase leading to the upper regions of the house. Panelled in white painted wood, the hall was at once cool and light, and a huge chest supported a vase of brilliantly hued orchids. Salvador appeared from a door across the hall, and saw them at once.

'Do you want anything, *senhor*?' he asked smoothly.

'Just – not to be disturbed,' replied Vincente eloquently.

'Of course, *senhor*!' Salvador gave a slight bow, and disappeared back the way he had come.

CHAPTER FIVE

SALVADOR's appearance acted like a douche of cold water on Dominique. What would he be thinking? she thought desperately. He knew she was engaged to John. Did he accept her assumed submission to Vincente Santos as something to be expected? Had he seen this same situation many times before? Dominique felt ashamed.

Wrenching her hand from Vincente's, she walked across to the vase of orchids, lifting one from its resting place, and placing it against her lips. Its petals were a delicate shade of purple edged with a darker shade which might have been black, and were curved exquisitely. She realized she was trembling and her weakness infuriated her.

She glanced about the hall, almost surreptitiously, unconsciously searching for a means of escape. The balustrade which curved to the upper floors of the house was a delicately filigreed wrought iron, and she realized perceptively that it was up this staircase that he intended taking her. Already he had moved to its foot, and when she cast a furtive glance behind her, she found him leaning on the balustrade watching her with lazy eyes.

'How old are you, Dominique?' he asked, almost compulsively.

Dominique bit her lip. 'Twenty-two,' she replied stiffly.

'Twenty-two?' he echoed disbelievingly. 'Incredible!'

Dominique swung round, infuriated by his attitude. 'Why? Because I still have some morals left? Because I don't just fall into your arms?'

Vincente half-smiled. 'Your words are as old-fashioned as

your inhibitions,' he remarked mockingly.

'At least I have some left!' she said angrily.

Vincente shrugged. 'And Harding? How do you see him?'

'What do you mean?' Dominique was curious in spite of herself.

'I mean – do you see him as other men? Or do you perhaps believe he is one of the – er – untouchables?'

Dominique frowned. 'I don't understand.'

'Do you not? Do you think perhaps that your man Harding is the most faithful of fiancés?'

Dominique stiffened. 'John is not interested in women – not – not as you are!'

Vincente's eyes darkened angrily. '*Madre de Dios!* You do not know what manner of man I am!'

'Yes, I do.' Dominique glared at him. 'It's obvious!'

Vincente approached her angrily. 'What is obvious?'

Dominique felt a thrill of fear surge through her veins. 'You are!' she cried unsteadily. 'Oh, why won't you accept that I don't want to have anything to do with you?'

Vincente caught her shoulders in a grip that bit savagely into her flesh. 'Stop talking like a fishwife!' he muttered violently. 'You know there can never be indifference between us! See – you tremble in my grasp! Is this a sign of indifference? Of contempt, perhaps?'

Her back was against the panelling, and he was very close to her. She knew if she gave in now she would be lost. She wanted to give in so badly, she wanted to wrap her arms round his neck and drag that mocking mouth to her own, she wanted to please him – to satisfy him. But she daren't, because she knew his intentions were most definitely not honourable ones.

With a supreme effort, she took him by surprise, pushing him sharply back, away from her, so that he fell against the polished chest, and was unable to recover his balance for a moment.

In that moment, she flew across the hall, to French doors that she thought might open on to the patio and safety. But they did not. Instead she was in the garden, in a part of the property that she did not recognize, and certainly could not distinguish in the darkness.

She halted, but there was no time to waste. She must get away. Sooner or later she was bound to see the lights of the patio, and Vincente Santos would be hardly likely to pursue her to his guests.

Ignoring his angry exclamation, she rushed across the terrace, down steps into the garden, and turned in the direction of a faint sound of music. Then she saw the lights, gleaming ahead of her, through the thicket of trees and shrubs in which she was standing. With a gasp of relief, she pushed through the trees, saw a faint, suspicious gleam of something silvery, and then screamed in shock and dismay as her feet encountered nothing and then icy cool water.

She sank down, spluttering chokingly, and emerged to the surface coughing. She was in the pool. Oh, lord, she thought. The ignominy of it all!

The water chilled her hot limbs instantly, and she gathered her wits about her and struggled to the side. At least it was no deeper than waist height where she had fallen, and it was comparatively easy to reach the side.

Then she heard voices, many voices, all chattering volubly and coming in her direction. But before they reached her, she felt someone's hands gripping her shoulders savagely, dragging her up on to the side of the pool.

'Dominique!' muttered Vincente's voice, and there was something more than anger in his husky tones. '*Dios*, are you all right? Tell me I have not harmed you!'

Dominique looked up at him. 'Vincente—' she began

weakly, and then the other guests came through the trees and surrounded them.

'Dominique!' That was John's voice. 'Whatever have you been doing?'

Dominique shivered a little. 'I just fell in the pool, John,' she said awkwardly. 'It was all my own fault.'

John looked at Vincente Santos. 'Is that right?' he asked, the whisky he had drunk that evening making him a little belligerent.

Santos nodded his head slowly. 'As – Miss Mallory says,' he replied suavely. 'Please, everybody, go back to the patio. This has been an unfortunate accident, but Miss Mallory needs to change – to get dry. Salvador will see to it, won't you, Salvador?'

Salvador seemed to appear from nowhere, and bowed his acquiescence.

John moved restlessly. 'Yes – but, hell, Dominique, how did you do a crazy thing like that?'

'Later, Harding,' said Vincente coldly. 'Later.'

John looked as though he was about to protest, but then Frederick Rivas took his arm and said:

'Come along. No harm has been done. We will hear all about it in good time. Come, let us have a drink. Coming, Vincente?'

Vincente gave Dominique a studious glance, and then nodded. 'Very well. Salvador, will you see Miss Mallory is adequately looked after?'

'Of course he will, darling,' said Claudia, taking Vincente's arm clingingly. 'Now, come and talk to me. I've hardly seen you this evening.'

Conscious of John's displeasure, Dominique followed Salvador drearily back to the house. She felt tired suddenly, and utterly dejected. Not only had she aroused Vincente's contempt by making a fool of herself, but she had drawn

John's attention to a situation that ought never to have happened. And what would he have to say about it? He was not going to be so easily placated this time. There were too many instances that Dominique simply could not explain.

Apologising for dripping water, Dominique followed Salvador across the hall where she and Vincente had talked earlier and up the shallow marble staircase. At least her premonition of ascending these stairs had not been misplaced, but in vastly different circumstances from those she had imagined.

The first flight of stairs opened on to a wide landing, carpeted in gold pile which spread into every nook and corner. Salvador crossed this landing and opened one of the many doors which opened on to it. Then he allowed Dominique to precede him into a luxurious bathroom, whose floor was marble mosaic again, this time in silver and gold. There was a deep sunken bath and a pedestal wash-basin in lemon porcelain, and the walls were lined with mirrors which gave back Dominique's reflection in hundreds of different angles.

Salvador indicated a door at the far side. 'That door opens into the bedroom which is part of this suite,' he said. 'If you will go through there after you've showered you will find something to wear.' He smiled. 'I will go now and arrange it.'

'Thank you.' Dominique pulled the wet dress away from her thighs, aware that it was clinging revealingly. 'I'm sorry to be such a nuisance!'

'Not at all.' Salvador bowed politely and withdrew. Dominique wondered if he ever showed his real feelings. No doubt he did with Vincente Santos. She could sense the affinity between them.

Then, shrugging these thoughts aside, she automatically locked the bathroom door and stripped off her clothes. It was refreshing to sluice away that awful clinging damp feeling under the shower, and afterwards she wrapped herself in the huge cream bath sheet which she had found folded on an ottoman. Then, smoothing back the tendrils of hair which had escaped from her braids, she walked to the door of the bedroom.

Gingerly she opened it, half afraid that Salvador might still be there, but he was gone, and lying on the huge bed was a silk dressing gown.

She glanced round. The lighting in the room came from a peach shaded lamp beside the bed, while the bedcovers were rose-coloured, like the drapes at the windows. A soft white carpet was underfoot, and rippled against her toes as she moved. It was a beautiful room, the furniture a light teak, with cut crystal dishes and candlesticks on the dressing table.

She stood for a moment, listening, but everywhere seemed silent up here, away from that side of the house where the party had been going on. She allowed the bath sheet to fall to the ground, and wrapped herself in the pale green silk gown. It was sheer and expensive, and clung lovingly to the curves of her body. It gave her a sensuous feeling, and she wondered rather wildly what she was expected to do now.

Then there was a tap at the door, and Salvador appeared again at her bidding. 'Ah,' he said, with approval, 'that is better, yes?'

'Much better,' agreed Dominique cautiously.

'Good. I will collect your clothes from the bathroom and have them dried for you. It will not take long, Miss Mallory. Do not look so alarmed!'

Dominique didn't know what to say, so she said nothing. Obviously Salvador was in control of the situation.

'Er . . . Mr. Harding . . .' she began awkwardly.

'Mr. Harding is with Senhor Santos's other guests,' replied Salvador. 'Do not concern yourself. He is being looked after, and has been assured of your safety.'

Dominique wondered. 'Do – do you have a cigarette?' she asked uncomfortably.

'Of course. In the box on the table beside the bed,' indicated Salvador. 'You would like something to eat, perhaps? Or a drink?'

'No, nothing else, thank you,' replied Dominique, shaking her head.

'Very well. You will excuse me?'

'Yes, yes, of course.'

Dominique nodded and turned away to help herself to a cigarette, aware that she was beginning to feel more relaxed with Salvador. She was getting used to his competence, and appreciating his silences.

After he had gone the room was very quiet. Dominique paced about restlessly, wishing the whole evening had never happened. She had made an absolute fool of herself, and no doubt John would think, rightly, of him too. But it hadn't been entirely her fault. Vincente Santos was the instigator. If his intention had been to ridicule her for some nefarious reasons of his own, he had certainly succeeded.

She drew on her cigarette deeply, walking to the doors which opened on to a balcony and stepping out. The sky curved overhead, a cloudless canopy of midnight velvet, the stars seeming larger and brighter than back home in England. The scents of the acacias enveloped her in their fragrance, and she leant her elbows on the balcony rail and sighed. It was such a beautiful night; it was meant for love, not for depression.

The sound of the door opening behind her brought her back into the room hastily, but it was only Salvador, carrying her folded clothes over his arm. As he had been gone for only about half an hour Dominique was amazed, and showed it.

Salvador smiled. 'I have a very adequate tumbler drier in the basement,' he explained easily, 'and a very competent press.'

Dominique smiled in return. 'I see. That's marvellous! Thank you, Salvador.'

Salvador laid the clothes on the bed, and straightened.

'Have – have Senhor Santos's guests left?' she ventured cautiously.

'No, *senhorita.* Why do you ask?'

Dominique shrugged. 'It's so quiet!'

'It is a big house, *senhorita.*'

'Yes. Yes, I suppose so.' Dominique fingered the material of her dress thoughtfully. 'I – I expect everyone thinks I'm a complete idiot!' she murmured.

Salvador halted by the door and looked back at her. 'Why should anyone think that?' he asked, almost gently.

'Well – falling in the pool and so on.'

'It was an accident, Miss Mallory. No one would fall in the pool fully clothed intentionally.'

Dominique bent her head. 'They might think I did it to draw attention to myself,' she said, sighing.

'I do not think so.' Salvador smiled again.

Dominique looked at him fully. 'Whose – whose gown is this?' she asked, unable to prevent the question.

Salvador shrugged. 'It belonged to the Senhorita Isabella, Miss Mallory.'

'Isabella?' Dominique swallowed hard. 'Who is she?'

'Senhor Santos's sister, Miss Mallory.'

'Oh, yes!' Dominique nodded. 'She entered a convent, didn't she?'

'That is correct, Miss Mallory.'

Dominique gave him an exasperated look. 'You're not a

gossip, are you, Salvador?'

'No, Miss Mallory. I try not to be.'

'But surely you realize that I'm trying to – well – learn things from you!'

'I realize that,' Salvador spread his hands expressively. 'However, I suggest if you want to learn about Senhor Santos's family you ask him.'

'You think he would tell me?'

'I think he would do a lot of things for you, yes, Miss Mallory.'

Dominique grimaced. 'Because he can't bear to be thwarted!'

'Thwarted? What is that?'

'Oh, never mind!' Dominique ran a hand over her hair wearily. 'Am I expected to get dressed and join the guests again?' Her tone was sardonic.

'If you wish.'

Salvador opened the door, and was about to leave the room when a shadow appeared on the landing, and then Vincente Santos was standing in the doorway, looking at them.

'Salvador,' he said questioningly. 'You were so long . . .'

'We have been talking, *senhor*,' replied Salvador calmly. 'Did you want me?'

Vincente's eyes were narrowed, as he looked across at Dominique. 'No, I was curious, that is all. Is our guest recovered? What were you talking about?'

'This and that,' replied Salvador, much to Dominique's relief. 'Shall I go?'

Vincente nodded, and stood aside for Salvador to leave the room. Then he entered, and closed the door. Dominique stood by the bed, wishing she had had time to put on her clothes, even though she was aware that the silk dressing gown was vastly becoming.

87

However, Vincente did not attempt to touch her. Instead he drew out a case of cheroots and extracted one calmly, lighting it with deliberation, before placing the case back in his pocket.

Then he looked up, his dark face brooding, his tawny eyes surveying her almost indifferently, as though assessing her qualifications. Then he said, startlingly:

'I want you to break your engagement to Harding and marry me!'

'*Marry you!*' Dominique couldn't believe her ears. 'You can't be serious!'

His expression was withdrawn but intense. 'Oh, but I am,' he said calmly.

Dominique pressed the palms of her hands against her burning cheeks. 'This is ridiculous! You don't want to marry me! You don't *love* me!'

'I want you,' he said emotionlessly.

Dominique turned away, shaking her head in bewilderment. His lack of emotion was uncharacteristic, his indifferent way of stating such assertions was unnerving. She felt like a craft that has been forced out of a safe harbour and is being tossed on a wild and alien sea.

What manner of man was he that he could attempt to seduce her one minute and then offer her marriage the next? What were his motives? What extra motivations had inspired such a command?

'I love John!' she managed to say tremblingly.

'No, you do not,' he replied coolly. 'Do not lie to me, Dominique. At least let there be honesty between us!'

Dominique swung round. 'Honesty. Honesty! How can you talk about being honest? How dare you presume to come here and ask me to marry you, knowing full well that my fiancé is downstairs at this moment, accepting your hospitality, believing in your friendship!'

Vincente shrugged his broad shoulders. Then he looked at her squarely. 'There was never – can never – be friendship between Harding and myself,' he retorted bitterly.

Dominique continued to shake her head. She was shaken and disturbed. She was even finding it difficult to believe all this was actually happening.

'All right, all right, you don't like one another, but that doesn't give you the right to assume—'

'I've made no assumptions,' retorted Vincente, his voice hard. 'Oh, Dominique, stop deluding yourself! You want me – just as much as I want you! All right, you don't like to admit it, but it's true nevertheless! Why is it that women imagine themselves different from men in that way?'

'You're talking about lust!' exclaimed Dominique unevenly.

'So?'

'So you can't marry a person out of lust!'

'Did I say that was all it was?'

'No, but—' Dominique pressed a hand to her throat. 'It is – I know it!'

'I've told you before, you know nothing about me,' he said bleakly. 'Don't assume too much yourself. Give yourself time to get to know me!'

Dominique bent her head, her shoulders trembling uncontrollably. Vincente gave a muffled exclamation, and crossed to her instantly, grasping her arms and pulling her roughly to him.

'See—' he muttered fiercely, 'I'm trembling, too. This is not Santos's way, believe me! I have wanted many women – and I have taken them. *You* – I respect. *You* – I am prepared to give my name!'

Dominique's thoughts were incoherent. 'I should be honoured,' she whispered, half hysterically.

'Stop it!' He forced her chin up with one hand. 'Stop it!

Now – what is your answer?'

Dominique closed her eyes, the lids pale and fragile, arousing his compassion, so that he pressed his lips to her eyes gently, murmuring to her in his own language. She didn't know what he said, she didn't care, she was drifting into a lethargic state of mind, and should he at that moment have decided to possess her utterly, she would have willingly surrendered.

But Vincente was very conscious of the warmth of her body through the thin material of her gown, and he held her away from him, looking into her eyes, eyes that were drowsy with his lovemaking, and said:

'*Dios*, Dominique! Would you have me lose my self-respect as well as my self-control?'

Her eyes flickered. 'Oh, Vincente,' she murmured achingly.

Then, without warning, the door burst open, crashing back on its hinges heavily, and John stood in the aperture, glaring at them with eyes that were incensed with fury and jealousy.

'You swine, Santos!' he snarled violently. 'I'll kill you for this!'

Vincente released Dominique, and turned towards John calmly. He thrust his hands deliberately into the pockets of his trousers, and walked slowly across to the other man. 'Oh, yes?' he said imperturbably.

'God damn you to hell!' muttered John heavily, and brought back his fist and hit Vincente full on the chin with a shattering punch. John was a powerful man and the force of his blow, which Vincente made no attempt to defend himself against, sent him staggering back to measure his length on the floor at Dominique's feet.

'Vincente!' cried Dominique in horror, casting a venomous glance in John's direction. Then she sank down to the floor beside him, pillowing his head on her knees, smoothing his forehead tenderly.

'Get up!' shouted John savagely, standing over them. 'Get up and fight like a man!'

Vincente rubbed his chin with one hand, and Dominique looked up at John contemptuously. 'Are you out of your mind?' she gasped. 'Coming in here like this and acting like some – some – wild beast!'

John wrenched her to her feet. 'You're my fiancée, Dominique. What do you expect me to do? Finding you here with him – half naked!'

Dominique tore herself out of his hold. 'At least give me a chance to explain!' she cried, rubbing her wrist.

'And how are you going to explain it?' asked Vincente lazily, getting to his feet.

Dominique looked at him with tortured eyes. Then she looked back at John whose fists were clenched angrily.

'Dominique is my fiancée,' said John, controlling himself with obvious difficulty. 'Whatever you say you can't alter that!'

Vincente straightened, squaring his shoulders. 'Oh, no?' He looked at Dominique. 'And what have you to say to that, *carissima*?'

Dominique shook her head, and as John would have stepped forward she put herself between him and Vincente, unconsciously aware that it was the biggest step she had ever taken.

John was taken aback. 'Dominique!' he muttered incredulously. 'Oh, Dominique, *no*!' He stared at Vincente Santos. 'Dominique, he's only playing with you as he's played with dozens of women! Don't let him make a fool of you! For God's sake, come away with me now! I'll forgive you anything. Just don't ruin your life!'

Dominique shook her head. 'I – I can't, John.'

'Dominique, you're infatuated with him, that's all. All right, all right, I realize you're infatuated with him, but believe me you're making a terrible mistake!'

Dominique bent her head. 'Please go, John.'

John hesitated, looked as though he was about to thrust her aside and attack Vincente Santos again, and then with hunched shoulders he turned and went out of the room.

After he had gone, Dominique moved as far away from Vincente as the room would allow.

'Well?' he said. 'You have burned your boats, haven't you?' His tone was rather sardonic, and she looked at him bitterly.

'Yes. What will you do now? Forget you ever made that proposal?' Her breasts heaved swiftly under the silk robe.

Vincente studied her for a moment longer, then smoothed his hair with both hands. 'No,' he said definitely. 'No, I will not forget that.' He put his hand into his inside pocket and drew out a folded paper. 'Do you see this? It is a licence, a marriage licence. We will be married tomorrow by Father Pesquez, at the church of St. Michel.'

Dominique was confused. 'But – but – you couldn't be certain—' she began unsteadily.

'Oh, I was certain,' replied Vincente, straightening his tie and walking to the door. 'I suggest you get some sleep. This room is yours – for tonight. Tomorrow – well, tomorrow there will be different arrangements.'

'But—' she began.

'No buts, please. Now I must go and wish our guests farewell. Until tomorrow ...' He gave her a brief nod and left the room.

CHAPTER SIX

DOMINIQUE slept badly, but as she had not expected to sleep at all, she supposed she should feel grateful. After so many bewildering experiences her mind could not be expected to relax, and when unconsciousness did overwhelm her, dreams came to torment and confuse her.

Once, in that deep blackness before dawn, she was awakened by a strange, unnerving scream that penetrated her consciousness and brought her up in the huge bed, terrified. She couldn't imagine what it might be, and in this alien, savage place she felt alone, completely alone, for the first time in her life. Even the death of her father had not affected her this way.

Eventually, of course, she had to lie down again, and when another scream shattered the silence she realized with relief that it was not a human sound, but the cry of a mountain lion, something she had not as yet encountered.

But sleep was not so easy to achieve again at this unearthly hour, and Dominique got up at last and lit a cigarette. Pushing open the balcony doors, she looked out, the air cool and refreshing against her hot limbs. A faint rosy glow was gilding the horizon, and soon dawn would break over the valley, filling their world with light. Dominique leaned on the balcony rail and sighed. Was she really here, or was this just another nightmare? Was she really to marry Vincente Santos? Had the scene with John actually happened? She shook her head. It was unbelievable, incredible!

And what did she really feel about it? Did she really have any choice? She only knew that since meeting him Vin-

93

cente Santos had dominated her whole existence, in a way no man had ever done before. John she loved, in a purely affectionate way, but he did not inspire the emotions in her that Santos inspired, so that even being near him was a delight, and touching him an obeisance.

She stubbed her cigarette out jerkily. In spite of everything she might be making a complete fool of herself. After all, divorces were easy to come by these days, particularly if you had Santos's money. He had never said he *loved* her. He wanted her, oh yes, she didn't doubt that. But was that enough? And if she loved him, would it be enough for her, knowing his feelings were not irrevocably involved? Could she stand by and see him with other women, secure in the knowledge of the circle of gold on her finger?

She swung back into the room and paced about restlessly. If she had any sense she would pack her cases and leave, not for Bela Vista; her future with John was shattered now; but for England, where at least there were people and places she knew.

She lay back down on the bed, closing her eyes wearily. What was the good of even thinking such a thing? Santos would not let her go so easily even had she wanted it.

Unwillingly, she must have slept, for when next she opened her eyes it was brilliant sunlight outside and a glance at her watch told her it was already after eleven.

Eleven! Dominique slid off the bed shakily, and pressed a hand to her forehead. It couldn't be so late! And if it was, why hadn't she been disturbed?

She glanced round the room. Her clothes still lay where she had left them at the bottom of the bed, but she did not find the idea of putting them on again very appealing. Was this her wedding day, or was it not?

Then, as though on an invisible cue, Salvador entered the room quietly, as though afraid she might still be asleep.

When he saw her standing by the bed, looking hot and flustered, he said:

'Ah, you are awake at last, Miss Mallory.'

Dominique spread her hands. 'Yes. Honestly, Salvador, it's after eleven, isn't it?'

'That is correct.' Salvador was his usual calming self.

Dominique gasped. 'But – I thought – I mean – oh, what is going on?'

Salvador smiled. 'A moment, *senhorita*,' he said gently, and withdrew from the room.

Dominique walked to the balcony, wondering what he was doing now. She did not have to wait long to find out. Presently he returned with a tray. On it were two jugs, one of coffee, the other of hot milk, and beside them was a dish of hot rolls and curls of butter, and some fresh fruit.

'See,' he said. 'Relax, and sit down. Have some coffee. Then we will talk.'

Dominique hesitated, and then seated herself where he indicated, on a basket-work chair beside a small occasional table. Salvador stood down the tray, asked whether she liked her coffee black or white, and then poured it for her. She sipped it gratefully, accepting that Salvador understood her feelings. There was something infinitely comforting about his unassuming presence.

When she was relaxing, and tasting a fresh roll with guava preserve, Salvador said: 'Now, we can talk, *senhorita*.'

Dominique managed a faint smile. 'Yes, Salvador, now we can talk. Do you know what about?'

'Of course, *senhorita*. You are to marry Senhor Santos, yes?'

'Yes.' Dominique raised her dark eyebrows. 'You don't find this surprising?'

'Surprising? No, *senhorita*.'

Dominique sighed. 'Well, I do,' she said moodily. 'Why is

95

he doing it, Salvador? Why does he want to marry me?'

Salvador shrugged. 'That is not for me to say, *senhorita.*'

Dominique lifted her coffee cup, caressing it between her fingers. 'You think not? You don't think I'm entitled to some kind of an explanation?' Then she felt remorseful. It wasn't Salvador's fault that this had happened. It was hers, or perhaps Vincente Santos's. 'I'm sorry,' she said. 'I'm overwrought.'

Salvador stood with his hands folded, looking at her. 'Why do you find the idea that Senhor Santos should want to marry you so surprising?' he said at last. 'You're a very beautiful young woman. Besides, Senhor Santos does not do anything he does not want to do.'

Dominique looked up at him. 'How nice for Senhor Santos!' she remarked sardonically.

Salvador shook his head. 'Come, let us forget this kind of conversation. We have other, more important matters to discuss.'

Dominique finished her coffee, and poured herself another cup. 'Like what I'm to wear, for example,' she said sighing. 'My wedding dress is still in the trunk at the Rawlings'. It will need taking out and pressing—'

'That will not be necessary, *senhorita,*' replied Salvador calmly. 'Carlos this morning has flown to Rio for your wedding gown. He will be back very shortly.'

'To Rio!' echoed Dominique. 'But – I mean – how—'

'The Senhor gave him your measurements and there is a particular shop in Rio where the Senhorita Isabella used to buy all her clothes. Carlos will deal with everything. He and Madame Germaine.'

Dominique shook her head. 'I see.' She felt bewildered. 'The wedding? When is it to take place?'

'At three o'clock, *senhorita.* Afterwards, there will be a

Take these 4 best-selling novels FREE

as advertised on TV

That's right! FOUR first-rate Harlequin romance novels by four world renowned authors, FREE, as your introduction to the Harlequin Presents Subscription Plan. Be swept along by these FOUR exciting, poignant and sophisticated novels... travel to the Mediterranean island of Cyprus in **Anne Hampson**'s "Gates of Steel"...to Portugal for **Anne Mather**'s "Sweet Revenge"...to France and **Violet Winspear**'s "Devil in a Silver Room"...and the sprawling state of Texas for **Janet Dailey**'s "No Quarter Asked."

Harlequin Presents...

The very finest in romantic fiction

Join the millions of avid Harlequin readers all over the world who delight in the magic of a really exciting novel. SIX great NEW titles published EACH MONTH! Each month you will get to know exciting, interesting, true-to-life people...You'll be swept to distant lands you've dreamed of visiting...Intrigue, adventure, romance, and the destiny of many lives will thrill you through each Harlequin Presents novel.

Get all the latest books before they're sold out!
As a Harlequin subscriber you actually receive your personal copies of the latest Presents novels immediately after they come off the press, so you're sure of getting all 6 each month.

Cancel your subscription whenever you wish!
You don't have to buy any minimum number of books. Whenever you decide to stop your subscription just let us know and we'll cancel all further shipments.

Sweet Revenge by **Anne Mather**
Devil in a Silver Room by **Violet Winspear**
Gates of Steel by **Anne Hampson**
No Quarter Asked by **Janet Dailey**

Take these **4** best-selling Harlequin romance stories **FREE**

exciting details inside

---

reception for the Senhor's guests at the Hotel Bela Vista.'

'I see,' said Dominique again. 'Are – are there to be many guests?'

'Just Senhor Santos's close friends, and perhaps some of the staff from the plant.'

'Oh, no!' Dominique pressed a hand to her lips. She felt she couldn't meet John's friends after this.

'Yes, *senhorita*. Why not? Engagements are made to be broken.'

'That's not true.'

'Nevertheless, a great number are broken,' replied Salvador. Then he walked to the door. 'I will be back as soon as Carlos returns. In the meantime perhaps you would like some magazines? The Senhor is very busy, as you can imagine.'

'Yes,' said Dominique slowly. 'No, don't bother with the magazines, Salvador. I – I'll take a bath. It's almost twelve. Time will soon pass.' Even as she said the words the whole realization of what she was doing seemed to hit her and she was glad she was sitting. She doubted whether her legs would have supported her.

'Very well, *senhorita*. If there is anything you require, please lift the house phone.'

'Thank you.'

After Salvador had gone, Dominique peeled an orange and ate it listlessly. She was merely eating to stop herself from feeling so faint, and for something to do.

Then she stood up and undid her braids, combing out her hair with her fingers, so that it fell in silky waves past her shoulders. Then she went into the bathroom and turned on the bath taps. There was plenty of time and she added some bath essence that she found in a cut glass flagon. It was sweet scented and rather intoxicating, and she stayed a long time in its fragrance.

Afterwards, she washed her hair, and dried it by means of an air drier fitted into the wall of the bathroom. Then, wrapped in a towel, she entered the bedroom again.

Her breath caught in her throat as she saw what was there. In her absence Salvador had returned and hanging against the door of the wardrobe was a short white lace dress, with a scalloped neckline and long sleeves ending in a medieval point. There was a veil to go with it, mounted on a tiara of diamonds, and she lifted it incredulously, unable to assimilate that these were real jewels and not imitation.

On the bed was an assortment of flimsy underwear, and several pairs of nylon tights. There were also some white satin pumps with a medium heel, the type she usually wore.

She flung off the towel and wrapped herself in the green robe again, unwilling to dress too early in this climate. It was becoming very hot, even in her room, and she would be glad to get out in the air again.

Then there was a tap at the door and Salvador came in again. 'Well?' he said, showing some enthusiasm. 'You like it?'

'Of course.' Dominique bit her lower lip nervously. 'Is – is everything going according to plan?'

'Of course, *senhorita*. What would you like for lunch?'

Dominique shook her head. 'Oh, nothing, nothing. I haven't long had breakfast.'

'Perhaps a little salad?' murmured Salvador tentatively.

'Oh, no, nothing, honestly.' Dominique couldn't eat anything now. Not now!

'Very well. But you will have some wine, perhaps? To bring a sparke to your eyes, and some colour to those pale cheeks, hmm?'

'All right.' Dominique felt reckless. 'Yes, Salvador. If – if you will have a drink with me.'

'Very well, *senhorita*. Give me a moment.' He disappeared again, and when he came back he had a bottle of champagne in his hand. 'See,' he said. 'Only the best is good enough for the wife of Vincente Santos.'

'I'm not his wife yet,' replied Dominique wryly, but she liked his manner.

The champagne was sparkling and frothy and delicious, and Dominique thought a drink had never tasted so good. What a strange wedding day, she thought, as she clinked her glass with Salvador's. She could never have imagined a stranger one.

But time was moving on, and it was with a sense of apprehension that she saw it was almost two o'clock. Salvador saw her swift appraisal of the time, and said:

'You are not nervous now, are you?'

'You must be joking!' murmured Dominique self-consciously. 'Was a bride ever not nervous?'

'Perhaps not,' agreed Salvador, nodding. 'So – I will go. You can manage? You do not require a maid to come and help you?'

Dominique stared at him. 'You have maids here?'

Salvador shook his head. 'No. But I would get Maurice's wife to come to you.'

Dominique shook her head. 'It won't be necessary, thank you. I'd – I'd rather be alone. How – how will I get to the church? Will Senhor Santos—'

'Senhor Rivas has kindly offered to drive you there in his car,' replied Salvador smoothly.

'Senhor Rivas!' echoed Dominique. 'Oh, heavens, Salvador! What will everyone think? I came here to marry Mr. Harding!'

'But you chose a better man,' replied Salvador simply, and left her.

Later, her hair wound into its braids, with two tendrils curling by her ears, Dominique put on the lace wedding dress. It was the most beautiful dress she had ever worn, and it moulded her figure perfectly. She reflected that Vincente must have a very good eye for size, or maybe he was just very experienced in buying women's clothes, she thought disturbingly.

The tiara was last. It fitted over the coronet of her hair, and the veil was circular and of the finest hand-worked silk. She knew she had never looked lovelier, her tan complemented by the purity of her gown.

As she was standing, shivering slightly, in front of the mirror, there was another tap at her door. Thinking it was Salvador, she called: 'Come!' but it was not Salvador, it was Alicia Rivas.

'Senhora Rivas!' she exclaimed, in surprise.

Alicia came across to her. 'Oh, Dominique!' she exclaimed, her tone slightly awed. 'My dear child, you look absolutely exquisite!'

Dominique swung round. 'You think so?'

'Of course.' Alicia smiled. 'Frederick is ready and waiting for you downstairs. I told Salvador I would bring you down.'

Dominique hesitated a moment. 'Senhora Rivas! Please – you – you don't think I'm completely crazy, do you?'

Alicia Rivas studied her for a minute. 'Crazy, Dominique?' she murmured. 'I think we are all a little crazy when we are in love!'

Dominique twisted her fingers together. 'But what will people think? I came here to marry John. And now . . .' She spread her hands.

Alicia took her arm, drawing her out of the room. 'My child, there was no good in marrying Mr. Harding if you do not love him. Besides, Vincente is a law unto himself, surely you have realized this by now!'

Had she? Dominique could have smiled. Only too well!

They descended the stairs together. Frederick Rivas and Salvador stood together in the hall, Salvador strangely sombre in a dark suit, and grey tie.

'Well!' said Frederick, with a low whistle of approval. 'This is an unexpected pleasure.'

Dominique reached his level and smiled rather tremulously. 'I expect it is,' she said awkwardly. 'After all – yesterday—'

'Yesterday is a million years away,' said Frederick sincerely. 'I am glad my friend Vincente has found a woman to share his life with him.'

Dominique compressed her lips. 'You're all so kind. I don't know what to say!' Her voice broke a little.

'Don't say anything,' remarked Salvador dryly. 'It is almost three o'clock. You do not wish to be late for your bridegroom, do you?'

Her bridegroom! Dominique shivered again. Had any girl ever had a more rapid courtship? Or a stranger wedding day?

A huge black limousine waited on the courtyard outside. Today in daylight, Dominique could appreciate the view more fully, but her nerves were too tense to allow her to enjoy it. Instead she was seated in the back of the limousine with Alicia Rivas, while Salvador took the wheel with Frederick Rivas beside him.

The descent to the valley floor was hair-raising on such roads, and for a few minutes Dominique forgot her perturbation at the wedding in the pure thrill of excitement that gripped her as she looked back at the house which was soon to be her home. Her home? She shook her head as though to dislodge the sense of unreality she was feeling.

The church of St. Michel stood on the outskirts of Bela

Vista, a grey stone building with a tall tower in which bells chimed the hour. It could have been a church anywhere, thought Dominique, in surprise, were it not for the hanging bougainvillea around its doors, and the climbing liana that threaded its old walls. But it had a warmth of feeling, a sense of security, that was at variance with everything else she knew about Vincente Santos.

As her feet encountered the gravelled forecourt, she had the strongest urge to escape, but it was not from Vincente that she wanted to escape. It was from the eyes of the congregation who must certainly consider this the most peculiar wedding of all time.

Then Frederick Rivas was taking her arm gently, and saying:

'Dominique! Dominique! Are you all right?'

Salvador and his wife had already entered the church and they were alone.

She looked at Frederick, saw his anxiety, and suddenly relaxed. 'Yes,' she said, 'I'm all right. Is – is he here?'

'Vincente?'

'Yes.'

'Yes, he is here. Waiting for you.'

Relief swept through her. She had half believed he intended leaving her at the altar.

Inside an organ was playing, then the congregation rose at a signal and she began to walk down the aisle on Frederick's arm. She was unconscious suddenly of anyone's eyes but those of Vincente. Her veil hid her expression, and she waited with bated breath to see him look at her.

But when she reached him, he barely glanced at her while she took in the perfection of the dark suit he was wearing, not a morning suit, but material of pure silk that rippled as he moved. His thick dark hair was smoothed back, and his eyes were enigmatic.

The service began and she tried to follow what was happening. Only the pressure of his fingers when he placed the ring on her finger got through to her, and she stared at the circle of gold in wonderment. It was a wide, heavy band that seemed to cling to her finger. But it was beautiful; the most beautiful piece of jewellery she had ever possessed.

Then the service was over, and she felt Vincente's lips on her forehead, cool and impersonal. She stared at him, trying to see in his eyes some appreciation of the picture she made, but there was nothing to distinguish, and she felt dejected.

The register was completed, and they emerged from the church together, to the peal of the church bells that echoed melodiously round the valley. People gathered, offering congratulations, rice and confetti were thrown, and Dominique managed to thank several people for their good wishes. Claudia was there, looking rather regretfully at Vincente, and on the fringe of the crowd outside the church Dominique caught a glimpse of John.

But it was only a glimpse and then he disappeared, plunging into the crowd so that Dominique lost sight of him.

Then she was hustled into the limousine, Salvador at the wheel again, but only herself and Vincente in the back. The car moved away, the guests who had been invited to the reception at the Hotel Bela Vista went to get their cars, and Dominique cast a curious glance in Vincente's direction. He was sitting in his corner, morose and solemn, and she wondered with an awful sinking feeling whether he was already regretting his actions.

Deciding she must say something or burst, she said: 'Do – do I thank you for my dress, or ask you whether you like it?'

Vincente looked across at her with brooding eyes. 'Do you think I like it?' he asked.

'I – I don't know,' she said breathlessly.

His eyes narrowed. 'It's a beautiful dress. But I shall enjoy seeing you more – later.'

Dominique flushed. 'Don't spoil it,' she said uncomfortably.

'Spoil what?'

'Oh, you know,' she said, aware of Salvador in front of them.

Vincente glanced in Salvador's direction. 'What would you have me do?' he asked huskily. 'My friend Salvador can hear every word of this exchange. I prefer to make love in private!'

Dominique felt chastened. She couldn't believe he was serious. He was using Salvador as an excuse. But an excuse for what?

The reception at the hotel was a buffet meal, a kind of mixture of late lunch and early dinner. There were rolls and sandwiches, canapés and cocktail snacks, fruit and meat and fish. There was champagne in magnum-sized bottles and every kind of spirit imaginable. Vincente did not seem to drink much and as he and Dominique were separated by their guests she felt even more isolated than ever. Somehow she had thought he would be more lover-like. Last evening he had showed more interest in her than he was doing at present.

Deciding he was the most hateful pig imaginable, she set out to charm every man that came within range of her. Frederick Rivas seemed enchanted by her, and although she did not actually flirt with him she encouraged his attentions. Then there was a young man, called José Bianca, whom Vincente had pointed out to her the previous evening with Claudia. He seemed fascinated by his boss's new wife, offered her champagne cocktails and cigarettes and talked incessantly about Minha Terra, the plant and motor racing.

Dominique endeavoured to show interest, but for all her actions she had one eye firmly on her husband, and the women who seemed magnetized by his charm of manner.

Charming with everyone but me, thought Dominique angrily. Oh, why had she agreed to marry him? She had merely succeeded in making herself completely and utterly miserable.

The reception went on for hours, and it was about seven-thirty when Dominique found Vincente beside her. Ignoring him, she continued to talk to José Bianca, and only José's abrupt ending to what he had been saying when he became aware of Vincente's presence halted their conversation.

'Oh, do go on,' Dominique insisted, turning her back on her husband.

'Dominique, we are leaving!' Vincente's tone brooked no argument, and José looked young and embarrassed.

Dominique glanced round indifferently. 'Oh, but José was just explaining something to me,' she said, smiling silkily. 'I'll be with you in a moment!'

Vincente's fingers curved round the soft flesh of her upper arm. 'Now, Dominique,' he said, in a harsh tone.

Dominique looked up at him, saw the hard expression he wore, and shrugged herself away. 'Oh, very well,' she said, realizing that to antagonize him further would merely result in making herself look ridiculous. 'Where is Salvador?'

'We do not need Salvador,' replied Vincente softly. 'Come, say good-bye to our guests.'

Dominique's face was suffused with colour when they at last emerged outside into the cool darkness. Vincente put her into the front seat of the limousine, then walked round to slide in beside her. His thigh brushed against hers, but there was indifference in every line of his body. Dominique compressed her lips. She wanted to cry. It was so different from her foolish imaginings.

They drove away from the town to the road to Minha Terra.

'We will take our honeymoon later,' he said expressionlessly. 'We will go to Europe. You would like that, would you not?'

Dominique shrugged. 'If you like,' she said, with forced indifference.

She thought he half-smiled at this, his profile vaguely visible in the light from the dashboard, and she felt really angry. She was his wife. Why didn't he act as though he wanted it that way? He had said he wanted her. He hadn't had to marry her!

They reached Minha Terra quite swiftly. He was a comfortable driver, as well as a fast one, and soon the floodlit house came into view. He drove into the courtyard, switched off the engine, and then looked at Dominique.

'Well?' he said questioningly.

'Well what?' Her voice was taut.

'Here we are.'

'Hooray, hooray,' she replied sarcastically, and slid out without waiting for his assistance.

It was another beautiful night, the stars hanging low overhead, and a pale moon rising slowly. She felt cold suddenly in the lace dress. She wondered when she would get her other clothes from the Rawlings'. Sooner or later she would have to fetch them. Intuitively, she felt that Vincente would expect her to get them herself, if only to show that she was not afraid of their barbs.

He had left the car and was mounting the steps to the terrace.

'Come,' he said. 'I have something to show you.'

Dominique hesitated, then walked slowly across to join him. He had loosened his tie, and it hung loose, while several buttons of his shirt were open.

Her eyes on his shirt must have communicated her thoughts to him, for he said: 'It is hot, isn't it?'

'I'm cold,' she replied pointedly, and he half-smiled again.

They entered the long lounge, and crossed to the arched entrance into the hall. Although lamps were burning, there was no one about and Dominique looked at Vincente curiously. But he did not speak, and she was loath to say anything herself.

When he reached the foot of the staircase, he said: 'I trust there will be no dramatics tonight!' in a low lazy voice.

Dominique did not deign to reply. She was still seething with resentment from the reception, and when he shrugged and mounted the stairs she turned and walked back into the lounge.

She expected him to come back, to be angry with her, to force her to go with him, but he did not. And his footsteps faded as he mounted the stairs out of hearing distance.

Damn him, she thought angrily. Did he have to be so unpredictable? Going over to the drinks table, she helped herself to a generous measure of brandy and added a splash of soda. But when she tasted it, it was not pleasant, and she poured it away and made herself another, this time with only a touch of brandy. Then she seated herself on the couch and sipped it slowly.

It was very quiet in the room after the noise in the hotel, and there were shadows on the patio that moved and shifted in the faint breeze. She knew they must be the shadows of the shrubs, but even so she recalled quite clearly the screaming cry of the mountain lion the previous night and she wondered whether they ever came down near the house. It was unnerving, sitting there, thinking such thoughts, and eventually she got to her feet and going over to the French doors, closed them firmly.

Then she walked into the hall and looked up the stairs. Only a faint light glowed from a single lamp on the first landing, and she frowned, wondering where Vincente was and whether he intended appearing again that evening.

Her stomach contracted at the thought. He must appear. He surely didn't intend going to bed and forsaking her now!

Compressing her lips, she went back into the lounge and replaced her glass on the tray. She pondered whether she should have another, then decided against it, pacing to the windows and looking out.

The stillness, and darkness, and the complete isolation were a little frightening to a girl who had always lived in towns, and she wished Vincente were downstairs also. Even if he ignored her, at least she would feel safer in his company.

As her anxiety intensified, she gave an exclamation, and walking across the lounge she mounted the stairs slowly. On the first landing, she looked about her. There was the door to the room she had occupied the previous night, but where was Vincente? It was a long landing, and there were several doors.

Taking off her shoes, she tiptoed along the passage to where one door stood ajar. There was a light inside, and pushing open the door, she entered the room.

It was not a large room, in fact it contained only a single bed, and it was certainly not luxurious as the room she had slept in last night had been luxurious. She frowned. Was this where Vincente intended to sleep?

Shaking her head, she moved to the centre of the room. Where was he? Was this another subtle means of tormenting her?

'What are you doing in here?' asked a voice suddenly, and

she almost jumped out of her skin.

'Vincente!' she exclaimed, swinging round to face him.

He was fresh from the shower, his dark hair still damp and tousled, while his only garment was a white knee-length bathrobe. He looked more attractive than she had ever seen him and her heart turned over. His eyes were sombre, however, and he said again: 'What are you doing?'

Dominique hid her nervousness. 'I – I was looking for you!' she snapped.

'Oh, really? Why?'

'Why? You ask me why when you've been up here about half an hour, leaving me alone down there with those awful shadows and every sound sounding like a thundercrash!'

'I invited you to come up with me!' he reminded her.

'Oh, yes? I remember! At least, I remember the sarcasm!' Dominique was breathing swiftly. 'Do you think you can treat me like an imbecile?'

He shrugged. 'What are you trying to say?'

Dominique bent her head. 'Oh, stop it, stop it!' she cried. 'You've deliberately tormented me today – done everything in your power to hurt me! Why are you doing it? Why?' Her voice broke.

His voice was husky as he said: 'What would you have me do?'

Dominique gave a muffled gasp and brushed past him on to the landing. 'Oh, I hate you, I hate you,' she cried bitterly. 'I wouldn't have believed any man could be so unfeeling!'

Vincente caught her wrist in a vice-like grip. 'Come here,' he commanded firmly. 'I'll show you our room.'

'*Our* room?' she echoed hysterically.

'Yes.' He drew her back into the small bedroom, and through it to the door at the far side. 'This is just a dressing-room,' he said. 'I've used it in the past. But this is the master bedroom.'

He threw open the door and Dominique stepped on to a cream carpet into which her feet sank luxuriously. The bed was massive, with heavy silk bed covers in blue and gold, while silver-blue curtains hung at the tall windows. And when she moved slowly across to the windows she realized they overlooked the valley below.

Vincente folded his arms, then said: 'Well? Do you like it? It's not been used before.'

Dominique swung round. 'Of – of course.' Then she looked at him pleadingly. 'Vincente! Tell me why you've changed!'

He closed the door. 'I haven't changed,' he muttered harshly.

Dominique turned away. 'How can you say that? Unless those other times have all been lies—'

She felt him close behind her, then his arms slid round her almost compulsively, pressing her back against him, while his mouth sought the tender nape of her neck. She allowed her body to rest against him, all resistance ebbing out of her.

'You told me I couldn't make you jealous,' he muttered, near her ear. 'But I have, haven't I?'

Dominique found it hard to breathe. 'Hmm,' she murmured, her eyes half-closed.

'Every time I've touched you, you've always denied your need of me,' he continued, his mouth seeking her throat. She felt his hands tearing the pins out of her hair, and as the braids fell, he threaded his hands in them, loosening her hair completely. 'So today I deliberately treated you to the kind of treatment you usually give me. I wanted you to want me just as much as I've wanted you, and now you do, don't you?'

'Vincente,' she groaned, twisting round in his arms, seeking his mouth with hers.

'Are you hungry?' he asked, burying his face in her hair, sliding the lace gown carelessly from her shoulders, allowing it to fall about her feet.

'Are you?' she whispered, against his mouth.

'Only for you,' he muttered violently. 'You are the most beautiful thing in my whole life! God, Dominique, I want you!'

Then he swung her up into his arms and carried her to the bed. She lay looking up at him with sleepy eyes, eyes drowsy with emotion.

'Love me, Vincente,' she murmured achingly.

'I intend to,' he replied huskily, loosening the cord of the bathrobe.

CHAPTER SEVEN

SUNLIGHT slatted through the blinds and one particularly persistent ray pierced Dominique's consciousness, arousing her unwillingly from a glorious sense of inertia. Her eyes flickered open, registering the blue and gold elegance of the room, and realization of where she was immediately flooded her being.

She turned her head swiftly, but she was alone in the huge bed, and only the rumpled pillows beside her bore witness to Vincente's occupation. She sighed, then putting her arms behind her head she allowed her mind to dwell on the events of yesterday with pleasurable recollection.

Then she heard water running and she realized Vincente must be in the adjoining bathroom. Sliding out of bed, she looked about for something to wear, and found his bathrobe at the foot of the bed. Wrapping it round her she went to the bathroom door, and then hesitated. She couldn't just walk in.

She was hesitating on the point of going back to the bed when the door opened and Vincente himself emerged. He was wearing dark slacks, his tanned chest bare, and he looked at her rather tenderly.

'Did I wake you?' he murmured questioningly.

Dominique shook her head, then she rushed to him, sliding her arms around his middle, pressing her cheek against his chest.

'Oh, Vincente,' she whispered. 'I love you!'

His hands cupped her head, then he bent his mouth to hers. 'Dominique, I've got to go to the plant,' he muttered huskily. 'It's the board meeting this morning. I've got to be there, unfortunately.'

'So early?' she asked, looking up at him appealingly.

'Early? Dominique, it's near eleven!'

'Is it? How terrible!' Her eyes were wide and innocent.

Vincente's fingers caressed her shoulders through the towelling material of the bathrobe, but with a muffled exclamation he thrust the offending cloth aside and buried his face in the soft warmth of her bare skin.

Dominique wound her arms round his neck, conscious of the power she had over his emotions, and he said thickly: 'Dominique, I've got to go!' but his tone was less than convincing.

'Have you?' she whispered provocatively.

His fingers tightened on her arms. 'No,' he groaned unsteadily. 'No, not yet!' and he carried her back to the bed.

Later, after Vincente had gone, Dominique took a bath and then dressed in the black dress she had worn to come to dinner two days ago. It was the only garment she had to wear apart from the lace wedding dress, and she could hardly wear that.

She reached the hall, and looked about her expectantly. She didn't know much of the layout of the house, and apart from the lounge and the dining-room she was lost. Both of these rooms were deserted, and she was standing hesitantly in the hall when Salvador appeared. She breathed a sigh of relief at the sight of a familiar face and said:

'You must show me the house, Salvador. I don't know where anything is.'

Salvador smiled. 'You look very beautiful this morning, *senhora*,' he murmured, in a satisfied voice. 'I trust you slept well!'

Dominique blushed attractively. 'Thank you, yes,' she said contentedly. 'Has – has my – my husband gone?'

'Oh, yes, *senhora*,' replied Salvador definitely. 'He went with much haste.'

Dominique compressed her lips, unable to suppress the surge of emotion that swelled inside her as she recalled that Vincente was hers entirely, and she was his.

'I see,' she said, at last. 'Now – will he be back for lunch?'

'Maybe, *senhora*, but very likely he will be late. On these occasions he usually has a sandwich from the staff restaurant and waits until dinner for a real meal.'

Dominique nodded in understanding. 'All right, Salvador.' She walked to the lounge, then turned. 'Is there a car I could use after lunch? I would like to go down to the Rawlings', and collect my clothes.'

'The Senhor did not say anything about you going out,' said Salvador, with some concern.

Dominique shrugged. 'Maybe not, but I must go. I can't wear this dress for ever.'

Salvador frowned. 'I could go to the Rawlings' for you. No doubt Mrs. Rawlings would pack your clothes for me.'

'No! That is – Salvador, sooner or later I've got to meet these people again. I think it would be better sooner.'

'As you will, Senhora Santos!' Salvador sounded annoyed.

Dominique sighed. 'Try and understand,' she exclaimed, then bent her head. Of course she could say it was none of his business, but Salvador was not like a servant to her, he was a friend, and she could understand his feelings.

Salvador shrugged. 'Very well. But I will drive you down.'

'All right, I'll agree to that,' said Dominique, smiling.

'Good. And now – come! I will show you your domain, then Maurice will serve you lunch. It is a little late for breakfast this morning.'

The house was larger than even she had anticipated, with reception rooms and lounges, and even a library and study. In the library there was a huge stereophonic record player and a pile of records, both modern and classical, much to her surprise.

Upstairs there were two floors. On the first were the main bedrooms with bathrooms *en suite*. The second floor was devoted to smaller bedrooms and a large room which Dominique found herself thinking might be suitable for a nursery in future years.

The staff quarters and the kitchens were in the basement, and it was here, in a huge streamlined kitchen, that she met Maurice, the chef, and Juana, his wife. Maurice was a Frenchman, born and bred in Calais, but removed from his employment there, in a hotel, by Vincente, with generous offers of remuneration.

'He was not married then,' remarked Salvador, as they returned to the ground floor. 'He met Juana in Bela Vista.'

'How romantic,' said Dominique, smiling. 'He seems very contented here.'

'He is. All of the Senhor's staff are devoted to him,' replied Salvador firmly. 'He is a good employer, as well as a generous one.'

'You're biased!' said Dominique with a short laugh. 'Salvador, I've adored exploring the house, but as it's about eighteen hours since I had any food, I'm starving!'

Salvador looked apologetic. 'Of course, of course. I had forgotten. I am so sorry, *senhora*.'

'That's all right,' said Dominique easily. 'We're none of us used to the new arrangements yet, are we?'

Salvador smiled. 'You are right, of course. Look – go out on to the patio. You will find a table there, overlooking the valley. I will bring you some sherry and in a few minutes

Maurice will have lunch ready.'

'All right.'

Dominique strolled outside. As Salvador had said, there was a small glass-surfaced table standing near the low parapet, shaded by a huge striped umbrella, and she seated herself in a comfortable basket-work chair and viewed the panoramic vista with a great deal of pleasure. The town sprawled in the valley, and in the distance the chimneys of the plant could be seen. The tall blocks of flats looked like toys from this height, and she became so fascinated with the view that she did not hear Salvador until he placed a tray on the table. A tray with glasses and a bottle of sherry.

'Oh, thank you,' she smiled up at him. 'Come and sit with me for a while. You can tell me all about Vincente now.'

Salvador gave a short chuckle. 'I think not,' he said, shaking his head. 'However, I have work to do and if we are going out this afternoon I must get on.'

Dominique sighed. 'Oh, very well.' Salvador walked away and she poured herself some wine. Sipping it, she wondered whether Vincente had appointed Salvador as her keeper or something. Certainly he seemed to consider her welfare as part of his duties.

Lunch was a delicious meal. There was melon cocktail, fried chicken with rice, and fresh fruit salad. She drank several cups of aromatic black coffee that accompanied the meal and then felt like nothing so much as going back to bed. She had never taken a siesta before, but today she felt pleasantly lazy. She thought with longing of the blue and gold luxury of the bedroom she had shared with Vincente, then determinedly thrust these thoughts aside. She had arranged to go out and go out she would. After all, if she delayed her departure then Vincente would most likely return and she would not want to go out at all.

Thus it was that about three o'clock Salvador drove

her down the hair-raising track to Bela Vista. She was relieved in a way that he had agreed to drive her. She doubted whether she would have had the courage to take a car of this size round such dangerous bends. The cars she was used to handling were of much less generous proportions, besides having less speed under the accelerator. She sat in the front beside Salvador, and they talked casually, about Rio de Janeiro and London, comparing the cities without involving personalities.

Bela Vista looked exactly the same, rather quiet for the time of day, and Dominique wondered why she had imagined that everything would have changed. It was just that she seemed to have changed so much herself that it seemed incredible that things should still be normal.

When they neared the Rawlings' house, she said: 'Don't drive me right to the gate. I – I'd rather be alone.'

Salvador looked disapproving. 'Why?'

'I can't explain, exactly. It's just that – well—' she shrugged. 'It somehow looks so – so – blatant!'

Salvador sighed, but he halted the car some distance from the Rawlings' gate. 'And what about your trunks?' he asked. 'Can you carry them?'

Dominique compressed her lips. 'No – no, I didn't think of that.'

'Then perhaps you should.'

She looked at him in exasperation. 'All right, all right, Salvador. Give me time to arrange it all and then I'll come to the gate and wave. When I do, you can drive along for my things.'

'All right. If that is what you want?'

'It's what I want,' she nodded.

She felt very self-conscious in the black dress which could not be described as a day dress, and she walked hurriedly past the gates of the other houses in the row. The Rawlings' house looked as drab and nondescript as ever, and she entered the garden nervously, walking up to the veranda slowly.

Then she saw, through the open French doors, Marion Rawlings and Mary Pedlar sitting together drinking tea. Her heart sank. Mary Pedlar would have to be here, she thought uncomfortably. Whatever would she say to them?

As though becoming aware of her presence, they both looked up and saw her, and Marion got to her feet and came to the window.

'Well, well,' she said spitefully. 'Going slumming?'

Dominique sighed. 'Of course not, Marion. I – I've come for my things.'

'Have you now? And where's your *charming* bridegroom?'

Dominique mounted the steps to the veranda. 'He's at the plant. There's a board meeting.'

'Oh, of course. He would have to be there for that. How disappointing for you! Your first day, too!'

Dominique reached Marion and they looked at one another, Marion dropping her eyes first. 'Well, you'd better get them,' she said grumpily. 'What do you think of this affair?' This to Mary Pedlar.

Mary shrugged her narrow shoulders. 'What do you think?' She looked at Dominique. 'Don't you think you've played a pretty filthy trick on John?'

Dominique flushed. 'Yes, yes, I do, as a matter of fact,' she replied quietly. 'But it would have been an even worse thing to do to marry him knowing I didn't love him!'

Mary Pedlar snorted, '*Love* him? Oh, grow up, Dominique! Love doesn't last in this climate – in any climate, come to that! You're too much of a romantic! Men aren't like women. They soon tire of people – places. *Wives!*' She looked up at Marion.

Marion nodded. 'That's true! You don't imagine Vincente Santos *loves* you!'

Dominique's nails were sharp against her palms. 'I don't think you're in any position to judge what our relationship involves,' she said tautly.

Marion laughed sneeringly. 'Oh, Dominique! I thought you were a woman of the world, with your short skirts and modern ideas! But you're just a silly little innocent at heart, aren't you! Good lord, there are such things as divorce courts, you know. You're not his first wife!'

Not his first wife!

Dominique controlled the passionate outburst that this statement invoked. It couldn't be true! Vincente hadn't been married before! He would have told her! Salvador would have told her!

But would they? Vincente had told her very little actually about himself, and Salvador was uncommunicative at the best of times. He would not tell her anything unless he had the say-so from Vincente Santos.

She must have turned pale because Mary said, with some concern, 'Are you all right, Dominique? You look ghastly!'

Dominique managed to square her shoulders. 'Yes – yes, I'm fine,' she replied automatically. 'If you'll excuse me ... I'll get my things.'

Marion nodded, giving Mary a speculative glance, and Dominique walked shakily through to the bedroom which had been hers. Once inside, she sank down on to the bed, knowing that her legs would give out on her if she didn't sit down. *Vincente married before!* The knowledge spun tortuously in her brain. But to whom? And when? And where was the woman now? Obviously he had divorced her – or maybe she had divorced him! Had they had any children? Was he already someone's father?

Her head was spinning with so many unanswered questions and her hands were clammy with perspiration. A rivulet of sweat seemed to be running down her back, while when she touched her head it felt fiery.

Oh, God! she thought sickly. Why didn't he tell me? How could he let me find out like this? So cruelly! Was this what Salvador had been afraid of when he tried to persuade her not to come down to the Rawlings'? Had he wondered whether Marion would blurt out such a shocking piece of information?

Her lips were dry, but she fumbled in her bag and lit a cigarette, wetting her lips to stop it from sticking to them. The nicotine temporarily soothed her, and she realized she would have to make the effort and collect her belongings together. Fortunately, most of her clothes had not been unpacked, personal belongings too had remained in the trunks, and there were only several crushable dresses and suits to pack.

Somehow, with trembling fingers, she managed to fold away the things, collected her toiletries from the bathroom and pushed make-up into the sponge bag, too. She worked automatically, not consciously giving herself time to think of anything.

When it was done, she emerged from the bedroom and walked unsteadily down the hall to the lounge door. Marion and Mary were still talking, but as she neared the room she realized they were speaking more quietly together, and when she heard her own name mentioned she halted uncertainly. More than anything at that moment, she wanted to know what they were saying, and no matter how unethical it was, listening in corridors, she must know what other gossip they were concocting.

'Obviously Dominique doesn't know about John,' Marion was saying softly. 'I feel sorry for her in a way, in spite of everything. After all, Santos is only using her to take his revenge on John for what he did to Isabella!'

Mary sniffed. 'I know. Everyone has realized that, I think.' She sighed. 'We could have told her – if she'd have believed us!'

'Well, we didn't have a chance,' muttered Marion. 'Anyway, Isabella was as much to blame as John. Hysterical creature! These Latin types are all the same. Treat everything as though it was a religion!'

'I know. I mean – entering the convent and all! Ridiculous really. I'm quite sure John didn't encourage her.'

'Of course he didn't! Heavens, if a man can't be friendly with a woman without her imagining he's passionately in love with her – well—'

'Even so,' said Mary, in a low tone, 'we were all surprised at the way Santos took it at the time. I mean – I thought he would have fired him, didn't you?'

'Hmm, I suppose so. But obviously he had other plans. What I don't understand is – why marry her? Why go so far as that?'

Mary clucked her tongue. 'Well, I suppose in a place this size he has to consider some of the conventions. Maybe he tried the other thing, but she wasn't having any, and – well, forced seduction is a crime, isn't it?'

'Hmm!' Marion sounded thoughtful. 'You're right, of course. Poor John, he's distraught! He was here last night – he stayed the night. You could tell what he was thinking – her up there – at Minha Terra – with *him*!'

Dominique stifled a groan, lying back against the wall outside the door feeling positively nauseated. It couldn't be true! It just couldn't be true! The things those women were saying – *they just couldn't be true*!

And yet every word they had said was reasonable.

All of a sudden she recalled Vincente's attitude the night

in Rio at his apartment when she had picked up the photograph of his sister. The way his voice had changed when he spoke of her. His antagonism towards John which was more than mere jealousy of John being engaged to *her!* She doubted now whether he had been jealous of John. Indeed, if what Marion and Mary said was true, everything was different.

She pressed a hand to her forehead, trying to get things into perspective. He had been attracted to her, she couldn't have mistaken that. She could arouse him – but only physically, her mind taunted her. She was an attractive woman, she was not conceited in thinking that, and Vincente Santos had always had an eye for an attractive woman. Everyone said so.

She twisted her hands together, tormentedly. So where did that leave her? And what sort of a future could she hope for? A few weeks – months, even – of his time, and then what? Separation? Divorce? Her life in ruins?

'Oh, no,' she moaned inwardly. *'Oh, no!'*

She tried to find some loophole in what they had said, but her innate sense of insecurity where Vincente was concerned had returned, and she couldn't believe that he had married her for any other reason than revenge. After all, there were many more beautiful women in Brazil, women who would fall over themselves to have him take some interest in them. That woman in Rio – Sophia. And Claudia here, in Bela Vista. They were only two of many.

And there was still the undeniable fact of his previous marriage. And the woman he had married!

Straightening, she endeavoured to assume an outward appearance of normality, and making sure they heard her this time she pretended to approach the lounge door and went in, saying:

'I've finished packing. Salvador is waiting with the car up

the road. I'll ask him to come—'

But she didn't need to finish the sentence because Salvador himself appeared in the French doors at that precise moment.

'You are ready, *senhora?*' he asked quietly.

Dominique nodded, somewhat jerkily, then going to the hall door indicated to him which was her room. Salvador collected the trunks in two journeys and while he deposited them in the car, Dominique waited with Marion and Mary.

'Aren't you having a honeymoon?' Mary asked conversationally.

Dominique compressed her lips for a moment, and then she said: 'Perhaps – perhaps later. We – we hope to go to Europe.' The words sounded empty and unreal. As empty and unreal as her marriage, she thought sickly.

'How nice!' That was Marion, not quite so jeering now.

Maybe they felt pity for her, thought Dominique faintly. She couldn't bear that. With forcedly nonchalant steps she reached the doors.

'Well,' she said unevenly, 'I – I must be going.'

'I'll tell John you called,' said Marion pointedly.

Dominique nodded. 'Tell him – tell him – I'm sorry,' she murmured.

'All right, I'll tell him. But I doubt whether he'll get much satisfaction from that,' said Marion dryly. 'Good-bye – *senhora!*'

'Good-bye.'

Dominique ran hastily down the veranda steps and across the turf to the gate. She slid into the car realizing she was shaking violently, and wondered whether nerves could cause a complete breakdown in the course of a few hours.

Then she chided herself angrily. Was she such a weak-willed creature that she would allow her nerves to get the better of her? Now was the time for her to be strong. She must not allow Vincente Santos – she could no longer think of him as her husband – to get the better of her!

Salvador got back into the car and looked at her strangely. 'What is wrong?' he asked. 'What did those women say to you?'

'Nothing.' Dominique was almost rude in her abruptness.

Salvador set the car in motion with controlled movements. Then he said: 'I am not a fool, *senhora*. Something has happened. Something has upset you – very badly, I think.'

Dominique glanced resentfully at him. 'You're so astute, aren't you, Salvador?' she said angrily.

'Astute? Astute? What is this?'

'It means you're always one jump ahead of me, aren't you? You didn't want me to come down here! You didn't want me to collect my own clothes? Why? Tell me that! Why?' Dominique took out a little of the pain she was feeling on him.

Salvador's fingers tightened on the wheel. 'You could have left it to me,' he said quietly. 'It is my job.'

'Your job! Your job!' Dominique was finding it difficult not to give way to the tears of humiliation that were pressing burningly against her eyes. 'What is your job, Salvador? To protect your master from the unpleasant results of his actions? Or to build a wall of pretence around the unpalatable things in his life!'

'I do not understand you, *senhora*.' Salvador was infuriatingly calm.

'Of course you do,' she cried bitterly. 'You knew that sooner or later I would discover the truth. You wanted to make it later. After all, the longer I could be fooled the greater would be the humiliation, wouldn't it?'

Salvador frowned. 'You are distraught, *senhora*. The heat—'

'Damn you, it's not the heat!' she gasped angrily. 'Oh, I wish I were dead!'

Salvador drove smoothly through the Rua Carioca and out on to the road that led into the mountains to the Santos house. Dominique took out her cigaretttes and lit one with trembling fingers. And as she did so she tried to compose herself. It was no good ranting and raving at Salvador. If he were to blame at all it was only indirectly, and she was making a fool of herself losing control like this. That was not the way. Somehow she must become as calm as he was. Only then would she be able to stand what must follow.

Salvador sensed her determined attempt to assume composure, and said: 'Whatever it is you have been told, *senhora*, I would suggest you wait until you hear the whole truth.'

Dominique glanced at him. 'And who will tell me that? Not Vincente Santos!'

'You think not?'

Dominique shook her head. 'How can I believe a man who has only married me because – because—' She halted. She would not discuss it with Salvador, no matter how great the temptation.

Salvador frowned. 'You think perhaps the Senhor marries lightly?' he exclaimed with some astonishment.

Dominique glared at him. 'You don't, I gather.'

'No, *senhora*.'

Dominique stared out of the car's windows, wishing with a powerful longing that the car would suddenly lose the power of its brakes and they would plunge over any one of these corners into the abyss of the valley below. Salvador would say anything to protect Vincente. She would not listen to his distorted explanation of how Vincente got rid of his first wife. She would listen to no more lies simply for self-preservation purposes.

She began to think coherently. She had been so absorbed in the effect this would have on her life, she had not even begun to think what she was going to do. What could she do? She was married to Vincente Santos. And there wasn't a chance of having the marriage annulled in this alien country. He held all the cards. He had the power, the affluence, the overwhelming influence on his side. She had offered herself to him, and now came the sacrifice.

The limousine swept into the courtyard of Minha Terra and Dominique wondered if her legs would support her when she slid out and walked swiftly across to the terrace. She glanced back, saw Salvador following her carrying two of her cases, and then ran up the steps and into the lounge.

She halted abruptly as Vincente rose from a low couch at her entrance and stood looking at her. Colour spread up her neck and over her cheeks, and she wished desperately that she had thought to change the black dress. She must look quite ridiculous for this time of day. Vincente, in his dark suit, his shirt collar unfastened, looked cool and attractive, and completely in control of himself.

And why shouldn't he be? she thought a trifle wildly. He thought she was still his gullible, adoring wife!

'Where have you been?' he asked. Was there censure in his tone?

'To the Rawlings'!' she replied, in a tight little voice, 'Why?'

'For my clothes, of course!' She endeavoured to control the surge of anger that was overtaking all other emotions rapidly.

'Salvador could have got them,' he said dispassionately, his eyes narrowed, studying her. He seemed to sense that she was strung up and he made no attempt to get near her.

'Yes, he could. But I preferred to get them myself.' She heard footsteps behind her and Salvador entered the room.

'I'll put these in your suite, *senhora*,' he said expressionlessly.

Dominique shook her head, compressing her lips. 'No. No, don't do that,' she said sharply. 'Leave them – leave them in the hall!'

Now Vincente's eyes seemed dark with annoyance, and he waved a hand impatiently. 'Put them in the suite, Salvador,' he said curtly.

'Yes, *senhor*.' Salvador ignored what Dominique had said and went out of the arched exit. She saw him out of the corner of her eye, mounting the stairs, and her anger increased.

'Was that necessary?' said Vincente bleakly. 'Obviously you're upset about something, but there is no need for this childish display of temper.'

'Childish display of temper!' echoed Dominique unevenly. 'Is that what you think it is?'

Vincente walked across to the drinks tray. 'Have a drink,' he advised coolly. 'It will calm your nerves.'

Dominique hovered uncertainly near the door, aware that if she was not careful she would lose the small amount of composure she had achieved. He was so cool, so calm! Did he have any idea of what she had learned? He must have! He must have known that sooner or later she was bound to find out! Did he imagine by adopting this indifference of attitude he would reduce what she had to say to a lesser degree of importance?

'Vincente!' she said angrily. 'Don't try to humour me! You must have some idea of what it is that has upset me!'

He turned, leaning back lazily against the table. 'Marion Rawlings has doubtless been endeavouring to cause trouble,' he remarked cynically.

Dominique twisted her hands together, bending her head, and he shrugged, and continued: 'You once told me I knew what kind of woman she was.' He studied her intently. 'You know it, too.'

'Yes, but – well, this is different! This is something indisputable. Something that not even Marion could have dreamed up!'

'Are you sure?'

Dominique looked up. 'Of course I'm sure.' Then: 'Are you denying you've been married before?'

Vincente's face revealed none of his feelings. It was like a mask, and Dominique wondered with a deep sense of dismay whether she would ever glimpse the man behind the mask. Last night she thought she had reached the real Vincente, the Vincente that none of these women with their posturings could reach, but now she was uncertain, insecure.

Finally he said: 'No, I don't deny that,' in a bored tone. 'Is that what this demonstration is all about? Does that arouse such passion inside you?' He gave an angry exclamation. 'God in heaven, what has that to do with *us*?'

Dominique stared at him. 'You should have told me!'

'Why? Why? Would it have stopped you from marrying me? Would you have rejected my proposal on those grounds! For God's sake, Dominique, you're not a child!' He turned and poured himself a generous measure of whisky, and threw it to the back of his throat. 'Why is it that my previous marriage disturbs you so?' he muttered savagely. 'I was young – and foolish! I have learned by my mistakes!'

Dominique was shivering a little. 'Did – did you love her?'

He swung round, surveying her sardonically. '*Love?*

128

What is love? I doubt whether you have the faintest idea! Certainly it bears no resemblance to the paltry emotion you say you have for me, that is shaken to its foundations by such unimportant revelations!'

'That's not all,' cried Dominique, hugging herself to stop the trembling sensation that quivered through her body.

'Oh no? What else? What other dastardly deeds have I perpetrated?' He poured himself another drink. 'What a thrilling conversation you have been having! Didn't you attempt any defence on my behalf? Isn't that what a loyal little wife would do?'

Dominique faltered, 'I – I didn't enter into a conversation. I – I overheard—'

'Ah, the eavesdropper who never hears good of herself, or in this case of her husband!' He swallowed his whisky. 'Do go on! You have aroused my curiosity!'

'Why did you marry me?' Dominique almost whispered the words.

Vincente sighed. 'Don't you know?' He gave a brief, mirthless laugh. 'I'm sure you do! I married you to take you away from Harding.'

Dominique pressed a hand to her throat. 'You – you didn't!' she gasped.

'Didn't I?' Vincente frowned mockingly. 'I thought I did!'

Dominique turned away, burying her face in her hands. 'Oh, God!' she moaned. 'Oh, God! I wish I was dead!'

Vincente strode across to her and swung her round to face him. 'That's what you wanted to hear, isn't it? That's what you had already heard from Marion Rawlings, isn't it?'

'Yes!' Her voice was very faint.

'I thought as much. How delightful that woman is! I must send her some flowers some time. Black orchids, perhaps!'

Dominique looked up at him. 'How can you stand here and talk so – so carelessly about something that affects us both? Why? Why did you do it?'

Vincente's expression was contemptuous. 'Did not you learn that also? Was not Isabella's name mentioned?'

'You're deliberately making me defend myself!' she exclaimed tremulously. 'I suppose the best method of defence is attack!'

'Attack, then,' said Vincente coldly. 'What are your weapons? Do you know how well Harding knew my sister? Do you know why she has entered the convent – locked herself away from the world?'

'Do you?'

'Yes, I know.' He turned away. 'But do not imagine that my admittance of that fact is a confession! My reasons for marrying you are my own. Whatever they may be!' His voice was taut.

Dominique hesitated. 'Are – are you saying I could be wrong? Marion could be wrong?' she whispered incredulously.

He spun round, staring at her with his tawny eyes, eyes that burned her up with their intensity. 'And if I were?' he muttered.

'Well then—' her voice was husky with emotion.

'Well then – nothing!' he snarled. 'Do you imagine you can come here to me – accuse me of deceiving you, not only about my reasons for marrying you but also by not revealing I had had a previous marriage – a marriage I choose to forget – and then, by denying these accusations, regain your respect, and thus accept your belief in me again? *No!*' He smote his fist into the palm of his hand. 'The accusations were made – the doubt was there. I would not have believed—' He broke off as though angry with himself for beginning the sentence. 'Get out of my sight!' He ground out the words as though he could not bear to look at her.

Dominique walked shakily to the arched entrance to the hall. Then she looked back. She was shocked and uncertain, despising herself for wanting to believe in him again. His anger was so real, his bitterness so pronounced. She had either misjudged him, or he was a marvellous actor. She supposed the latter could be true. He had had plenty of experience with women, and would know instinctively the best way to deal with her. Even so . . .

'Get out!' he said violently, swinging round from the drinks tray and seeing her hovering there.

'Out?' she faltered. 'Out of Minha Terra?'

'Oh, no!' A harsh smile lit his cruel features. 'Not out of Minha Terra. You are my wife, Dominique, and my wife you are going to stay, like it or not! Do you imagine I am going to make myself a laughing stock by throwing you out on the strength of a stream of gossip that you have heard from that snake of a woman and which you have brought here and repeated to me? Oh, no, Dominique! If I am the man you think I am you will understand this. I haven't finished with you yet. You have no idea of the degradation I could bring on you if I tried!'

'Stop it! Stop it!' Dominique put her hands over her ears.

'Why? Why shouldn't I vent a little of my disappointment on you? You will find I can be completely ruthless when I am thwarted!'

'Are – are you threatening me?' Her voice trembled.

'Yes – yes, I suppose I am. At any rate you can go and unpack your things. In *our* suite!'

Dominique gnawed at her lower lip. 'You – you don't imagine we can – we can live together – after this?' she exclaimed.

'You mean sleep together, don't you?' he corrected her

savagely. 'Oh, yes, Dominique! As I have said – you are Santos's wife! And what I have, I keep.'

Dominique shook her head. 'You – you can't force me—' she began.

'Can't I? We'll see. Now get out!'

Shivering, she made her way up the stairs. She met Salvador on the landing, but she would not look at him. However, he touched her arm and said:

'Be careful, *senhora*. A man can only stand so much!'

Dominique's brows drew together. 'What do you mean?'

'Think about it,' replied Salvador quietly. 'And do not judge a man by any criterion but your own experience of him!'

Then he hastened down the stairs, and she was left staring after him, wishing with all her heart she had not gone down to the Rawlings' house today.

CHAPTER EIGHT

THE suitcases stood in the centre of the floor of the beautiful blue and gold bedroom, and Dominique entered the room wearily, and closed the door. So many things had happened since this morning, and it was impossible to try at this time, and in her confused condition, to assimilate them. Just as yesterday had developed into something exciting and satisfying, so today had developed into a positive disaster. Not only had she discovered a lot of incredible things about her husband, but she had also alienated whatever it was that had drawn him to her in the first place. And she did not doubt him when he said he could wreak vengeance. She had always been aware of that sense of primitive savagery about him, and she dared hardly consider what his actions might now be.

She sat down on the window seat overlooking the sweep of the valley below, and shivered a little, in spite of the heat of the day. What on earth was going to happen to them? How could she go on living with a man who had tricked her and who now seemed to despise her? She sighed. It was incredible that only three weeks ago she had been excitedly planning this trip to South America. Now she was a married woman, married to a Brazilian whom she neither knew nor understood, and who would not think twice before destroying her. And yet she loved him!

That was the agony of it all! She loved him!

Even Marion's malicious words could not destroy that, and if she felt a sense of humiliation at his reasons for marrying her, it was because of her own disappointment, and not really to do with John and Isabella at all. Even his previous marriage, if she could get it into perspective, was something she could live with, if she had to.

Maybe if Vincente had not been here when she returned, if she had had time to sit and really think about what she had learned, she would have been able to act normally, and not treat him like some kind of monster. If she had seriously thought about the whole business, she might have been able to disguise the hurt and bitterness that Marion's revelations had aroused in her. After all, to her her love should be the most important thing, and if half a loaf was all she was to have, then that was better than nothing at all. If he had got some kind of sadistic pleasure in taking her away from John, then maybe he had his reasons, who could tell? As Marion had said, he was much more likely to take John's interest in his sister seriously, knowing how protective Latins could be towards their womenfolk, but at the time she had heard the conversation between Marion and Mary, newly informed of his previous marriage as she had been, it had been impossible to think coherently as she was doing now.

She got up miserably, and walking across to the table, helped herself to a cigarette, lighting it with fingers that shook. Whatever she thought, whatever excuses she tried to find for his behaviour, there was no altering the facts, and they were still as unpalatable as ever. He had deliberately deceived her, he had deliberately set out to attract her, right from their first meeting, and although she knew she was attractive, she was no *femme fatale* to sweep a man of his sophisticated tastes off his feet. No, there had to be a germ of truth in Marion's words, there was no smoke without fire, as they say, she thought gloomily.

With angry, nervous movements, she flung open her suitcases, and began to take out her clothes. For the present, at least, there was nothing she could do. As Vincente had said, she would stay, and she might as well make the best of it.

Who knew what might happen in the days to come? One thing was certain, however. Sooner or later she must speak to John, discover for herself what his relationship had been with Isabella Santos, so that she was not in the dark over that affair as she was now.

Later, when all her clothes had been hung away in the wardrobes, she bathed and changed into a slim-fitting shift of turquoise linen. It was one of her plainest dresses but nonetheless attractive, and after she had combed her hair, she gathered it into a chignon on the nape of her neck as she felt too tired to attempt to put it up. Even with lipstick, her features looked pale and she felt a sense of trepidation at the prospect of the evening ahead.

When she descended the stairs, however, Vincente was not around, and when Salvador appeared in the lounge to announce that dinner was ready, she said: 'Where – where is my husband, Salvador?'

Salvador gave his usual polite bow, and said: 'Senhor Santos is dining out this evening, *senhora*.'

Dominique couldn't believe her ears. After his anger earlier, combined with the fact of his not coming up to the suite to change, she had assumed he was still downstairs brooding. To find he had gone out was an affront to the trouble she had taken with her appearance.

'Where – where has he gone?' she asked carefully.

Salvador shrugged his shoulders. 'That I cannot say, *senhora*.'

Dominique felt a pent-up sense of frustration. 'For goodness' sake, Salvador,' she snapped, her voice unsteady, 'couldn't this just be one occasion where you betray a confidence? I'm his *wife*!'

Salvador twisted his hands together. 'But it is the truth, *senhora*. I do not know where Senhor Santos has gone.'

Dominique went across to the drinks table and poured herself a generous measure of whisky. She felt like drinking and drinking, a thing she had never done in her life before. Anything to provide a temporary sense of oblivion from the pain that was tearing her apart.

Salvador came over to her. 'I should not drink that, *senhora,*' he said quietly. 'It is very strong. It will probably make you sick.'

Dominique looked scornfully at him. 'Don't you think I've ever taken a drink before, Salvador?' she asked harshly. 'I'm not a child, you know.'

'I know you are not, *senhora,*' replied Salvador gravely. 'Nevertheless, I would advise—'

'I don't want your advice,' said Dominique bitterly, and raising the glass to her lips she swallowed half its contents at a gulp.

Immediately she almost choked, and a spasm of violent coughing racked her body, accompanied by a burning sensation in the back of her throat and the pit of her stomach. Her eyes watered, and she sought about desperately for a handkerchief. Salvador handed her his calmly, and after she had finished coughing took the drink from her unresisting fingers, and replaced it on the tray. Then he said:

'Dinner is served in the small dining-room, *senhora.* Will you come now?'

Dominique looked at him, almost impatiently, and then with a resigned expression she preceded him out of the room.

The meal was a silent one. Dominique ate little, and sipped the wine that Salvador provided with an absent air. Her surroundings, the warmth of the velvety night air, the scents of the stocks and the roses that grew in such profusion, meant little to her. She was absorbed with her thoughts and with the agonizing speculation as to where

Vincente might be. She knew there were plenty of women willing to comfort him, to desire him to make love to them, plenty of women always ready to answer his every need. He didn't *need* her. She had merely been a passing diversion, someone different, an alien face to satisfy his ego.

Leaving the table, she walked to the narrow wall that circled the patio and sat on its edge, sighing. Last night at this time she had been in his arms, known what it was like to have Vincente for a lover. And tonight she was alone, bereft, and whether it was of her own making or not, it was merely a precipitation of the eventual state of her affairs. Sooner or later he was bound to tire of her, and then . . .

She wanted to cry. So badly she wanted to break down and cry, cry for herself and Vincente, but most of all for the dream that had never reached maturity. And here she was, alone and practically friendless in a strange country without the means to escape from the situation in which she now found herself. She was no longer in control of her destiny. She had forfeited that when she agreed to become Vincente Santos's wife.

It was late when eventually she sought the comfort of bed. When she reached the first-floor landing she saw Salvador emerging from the room she had used that first night at Minha Terra, and she wondered whether the door had a key. It was something she had not noticed before, but now it became of primary importance to her. After the evening she had spent she could not bear the thought of him returning home, possibly from the arms of another woman, to find her waiting patiently in the master bedroom, like some subdued slave, afraid of its master.

She entered the dressing room which adjoined the master bedroom, wishing Salvador 'good night' as she did so. Then she closed the door and leaning against it, waited until she heard him descending the stairs again. When she heard sounds, she hastened into the big bedroom, collected her nightdress, then hastily crossed the landing and entered the smaller room. The bed had been re-made and she turned back the covers smoothly.

Then she went into the bathroom to wash and clean her teeth.

However, she had not been in the bathroom above five minutes when there was a tap at the panels. She almost jumped out of her skin, and grasping a towel about her she went to unlock the door and looked out – at Salvador.

'Yes?' she said, rather sharply.

'Why are you using this bathroom, *senhora*?' he asked.

Dominique straightened her shoulders. 'That isn't the sort of question one expects from a servant,' she said angrily, and instantly regretted the words as she saw Salvador's face grow withdrawn. She sighed. 'I'm sorry, but you haven't been exactly helpful to me this evening, have you, Salvador?'

Salvador relaxed. '*Senhora*, for your own good, sleep in the master bedroom. Do not be deceived into thinking you can defy him.'

Dominique bit her lip. 'If I sleep in this suite, I shall lock the door,' she said, trying to sound composed and failing miserably.

'You think perhaps a key would keep my master out?' asked Salvador sadly, shaking his head. 'Oh, no, *senhora*. Keys are for the weak man. Strategy is for the strong man!'

'Strategy?' Dominique frowned.

'Sleep in the master bedroom,' said Salvador again. 'Please.'

Dominique hesitated. 'Oh, Salvador! I wish I knew what to do!' Her voice broke.

Salvador shrugged. 'You are Santos's wife now, *senhora*.

There are many things you can do.'

Dominique shook her head. 'Not the things I want to do, though. I'm not even sure what Vincente intends to do. He's as unpredictable as ever.'

Salvador gave a slight smile. 'But you, *senhora*, you will wait and find out, yes? You are not so unpredictable.'

'Perhaps it would be better if I were,' she sighed.

'No, that is not so. There is an old Chinese proverb which says: "He who rides the tiger dare not dismount". You are like that man, *senhora*. You cannot escape from your destiny.'

Dominique bit her lip. 'Can any of us?'

'No, I suppose not. But there are some who think they can control it.'

'And you think – my husband is one of these?'

'I think the Senhor does not realize what he has in his keeping. He has not yet discovered its value!'

Dominique managed a wry smile. 'Thank you, Salvador.' She folded the towel closer about her: 'I – I was afraid you'd let me down—'

'This evening? Had I known where the Senhor was, I would have told you. You are his wife – and as such, you are entitled to know his whereabouts. I am not completely without heart, *senhora*.'

Dominique bit her lip. 'I can see you are not. I'm sorry if I was rude – before.'

Salvador shook his head. 'Get some sleep, *senhora*. Tomorrow is another day.'

Dominique did not sleep well. The bed seemed wide and empty, and her nerves were stretched to the utmost, conscious of every strange sound, every footfall about the house. But gradually the concentrated effort exhausted her and she fell into an uneasy slumber, only to be awakened harshly some time later by the sound of a powerful engine roaring into the courtyard of the house.

Immediately she was wide awake, tense and listening, waiting for footsteps on the stairs, outside her door, in the room.

But the engine was turned off, and a door slammed, and then there was complete silence, a silence almost deafening in its intensity. Dominique clenched her fists. If he was coming to her, why didn't he come? Didn't he know the sense of fatality that was overtaking her? Couldn't he know she was positively terrified, not only of him, but of her own treacherous emotions?

The silence stretched into infinity. Her stiff body was forced to relax, and she felt slightly sick from the strain. Putting on the bedside lamp, she glanced at the watch on the table. It was a little after two o'clock. She heaved a sigh. What was he doing? Was this some more subtle means of torment? If so, it was succeeding.

She turned out the light again, but eventually she must have dozed, because although she tossed and turned, and saw the faint pink rays of the sun piercing her balcony windows, morning at last came round, but he had not joined her.

She rose at seven, showered and dressed in cotton corded pants of a deep shade of purple, and a white sleeveless sweater. Then she combed her hair into a loop, pinned it in place, and descended the stairs.

There were voices in the dining room, and she paused in the doorway, nervously, seeing Vincente and Salvador talking together, Vincente seated at the table, and Salvador serving him.

Vincente rose politely at her entrance, and then as she joined him at the table, seated himself again.

'Bring more rolls and fresh coffee, Salvador,' he instructed the manservant, and Salvador withdrew after wishing

Dominique 'good morning'.

Dominique said: 'Just coffee, thank you, Salvador,' in a small voice, but she doubted her ability to give him commands.

Vincente had obviously almost finished his meal, and was in the process of smoking a cheroot with a cup of strong black coffee. Dressed in a lightweight tropical suit of cream linen, he looked cool and dark and attractive, and Dominique could not prevent herself from looking at him, rather surreptitiously.

'Well?' he said, at last. 'Did you sleep well?'

'Yes, thank you,' replied Dominique politely. 'Did you?'

'Reasonably well,' he answered coolly. 'I hope the car did not wake you.'

Dominique compressed her lips. He was baiting her and she would not satisfy his sadistic amusement.

'Car?' she questioned. 'What car?'

But Vincente merely smiled sardonically, as though he was fully aware of her pitiful attempt to deceive him. Salvador returned with a dish of hot rolls, a jug of coffee, and another of hot milk. He placed them conveniently beside Dominique, asked whether they required anything else, and then with a particularly gentle smile in Dominique's direction, he withdrew.

Vincente studied his wife. 'You seem to have succeeded in stealing Salvador's allegiance,' he remarked.

'I doubt that, very much,' returned Dominique, pouring herself some coffee with hands that were quite steady considering her nervousness.

'Do you? Why? I am such a monster, it is inconceivable that a man such as Salvador should not find someone more pleasant to be his – how shall I put it? – mentor.'

'Oh, don't!' exclaimed Dominique. 'Loook, this is rid-

141

iculous! We're sitting here, talking of banalities, when all the time the subject that is closest to the surface of both our minds remains unspoken! You've got to talk to me, Vincente. I've got to know where I stand!'

'And where do I stand?' he countered, in a hard voice.

'I don't understand.'

'Do you not? I think you do. I think you understand very well. You started this, Dominique. I did not.'

'How can you say that? I only repeated to you what I had been told.'

'Hysterically,' he amended cruelly. 'You were like a woman possessed when you returned here yesterday. You were in no mood for reasonable argument. You listened to that woman – that snake – and believed her completely, even though you know she has a reputation for just this kind of thing!'

'But you didn't help me! You let me say it all! You didn't try to explain.'

'Why should I defend myself to you?' He rose abruptly to his feet. 'I do not have to explain myself to anybody!'

'I am your *wife*, Vincente!'

He gave her an eloquent look, and then walked to the window, staring out broodingly at the view. Dominique's appetite, small though it was, fled, and she pushed the rolls aside and reached for a cigarette. When it was lit, she sipped her coffee, and tried to imagine what it would be like, going through weeks, months – even years, of this kind of relationship.

She wanted to ask him where he had been last night, but she doubted he would even answer her.

Then he turned and said: 'I have to go to the refinery today. What will you do?'

Dominique flushed. 'I don't know.'

'I wish to make it clear that I do not want you to go down

to Bela Vista again, without my permission.' His voice was cold as ice.

Dominique listened, felt upset, and then suddenly his words aroused her natural resilience. How dared he imagine, after all that had happened, that he could dictate her comings and goings! She looked up at him, and said:

'If I wish to go down to Bela Vista, I will go!' in a cool, composed voice, much different from the tumultuous emotionalism that was burning inside her.

Vincente leaned back against the window frame. 'You think so?'

'I know so!' Dominique sounded scornful. 'What will you do? How will you stop me? Tie me up? Lock me in my room? Are you afraid I may hear more of your short-comings?'

Vincente straightened, his face darkening, his eyes burning with his fury. 'Do not dare to speak to me in that fashion!' he snapped angrily.

But Dominique was gaining power from allowing some of her hurt and anger and humiliation to escape. It was a kind of release from tension, and she was not willing to give it up no matter how frightening Vincente might appear.

'I'll speak to you as I like,' she cried, getting to her feet. 'Until now I've been subdued, I've allowed you to take the initiative, to offer no explanation for your actions but anger. I've even imagined myself as the protagonist in this – black comedy! But no more. You seem to be forgetting! I am not one of your clinging Spanish/Portuguese *senhoritas*! I am English, and in England men treat women as human beings – not playthings – not useless vessels!'

Vincente crossed the floor to her side, staring at her with tormented eyes. He gripped her shoulders cruelly, shaking her violently.

'Stop this hysterical emotionalism!' he shouted. 'You

don't know what you're saying! You imagine because I do not plead with you to forgive me, make unnecessary excuses for something that should have absolutely nothing to do with us, that I am therefore trying to hide even greater misdemeanours. Grow up, Dominique! You are a woman now, not a foolish child! And I am a man – and I do not care to be treated like an *animal*!'

Dominique stared at him tremulously. 'Then tell me about John and Isabella!' she said.

Abruptly he released her. 'Obviously you have not listened to a word I have been saying,' he said heavily. 'Is there no trust in your whole body?'

Dominique hesitated. Always he was capable of arousing the uncertainties inside her. Already he had succeeded in subduing that rebellious desire to hurt him as he was hurting her.

'You want complete submission,' she exclaimed bitterly.

'I want a wife! Not an inquisitor!' His voice was harsh. 'Why do you continually concern yourself with what is past? Surely it is the future that should concern us?'

'Future? What future?' asked Dominique bleakly.

'Quite!' he replied cruelly.

Dominique moved restlessly. 'Then let me go.'

'Let you go? What does that mean? You want to be free of me, is that it? Free to rejoin Harding, perhaps?'

Dominique knew she could never go back to John, but he need not know that. She clung to a foolish sense of pride. 'Is that so inconceivable?' she asked. 'After all, he was my fiancé, he *loved* me!'

Vincente's face was contorted with his anger. 'That English pig does not know the meaning of the word!' he swore furiously.

'Do you?' Dominique stared at him.

Vincente gave her a strange look, and then he walked to the door. 'Oh, yes,' he said coldly, 'I know.'

Then he left the room, leaving her alone and unhappy, and as confused as ever.

The day passed unbearably slowly. Dominique wandered aimlessly about the house, touching a thing here, altering an ornament there, collecting flowers from the garden and replacing those in the hall and in the lounge, putting on her swimsuit and lying on a lounger by the pool. But there was no peace from her inner torment, and she could not stay long in one place.

In the late afternoon, when the bees were humming drowsily through the flowers, and the heat seemed to hang in the air like a tangible force, Dominique was lying on a lounger on the patio. She had managed to seduce her mind to a state of inertia, and a couple of magazines lay open on her lap. Then the telephone rang, its loud peal breaking into the stillness and banishing the quietude.

Dominique sat up and saw Salvador walking at his usual unhurried pace into the lounge. He lifted the receiver, and she settled back again. It could be no one for her. Maybe it was someone who thought Vincente might be at home, spending some time with his new wife.

When Salvador appeared in front of her, his impassive face unusually animated, she said: 'What is it, Salvador?' in a puzzled tone.

Salvador linked his fingers together. 'It is a call, *senhora*. From the refinery. It is for you.'

Dominique frowned. 'For me?' She felt a faint feeling of apprehension. 'Who is it? Vincente?'

'No, not the Senhor, *senhora*. Please, you come to the telephone now.'

Dominique shook her head. 'Whoever it is, Salvador, you

take the call. You give me a message. I don't want to talk to anybody.'

'But you must, *senhora*,' insisted Salvador urgently. 'It is important!'

Dominique sighed. 'Oh, Salvador, you know I don't want to talk today.'

'*Senhora!*'

Dominique shrugged her shoulders. 'Oh, very well. Who is it?'

'It is the Senhor Rivas, *senhora*,' replied Salvador, helping her to her feet.

Dominique relaxed. She liked Frederick Rivas. At least she was not nervous of speaking with him. She followed Salvador into the lounge and took the receiver when he handed it to her. Salvador did not leave the room, but waited by the door, and Dominique did not like to ask him to leave.

'Hello,' she said into the phone. 'This is Dominique Mall— Dominique Santos!'

'Ah, Dominique!' Rivas sounded relieved. 'Thank heaven you were there! My child, I have a terrible piece of news. There has been an accident in the laboratory!'

Dominique felt the blood draining out of her head, and an awful feeling of faintness enveloping her whole being. Grasping the edge of the table, she said: 'An accident? Senhor Rivas, what has happened? Has my husband been injured – he's not—'

'No – no, he's not dead. But yes – he is injured.'

Dominique pressed a hand to her throat, swaying a little, and Salvador crossed the room to her side to provide support should she require it.

'Go on!' she said weakly. 'What has happened? Where is Vincente? I want to see him.'

All of a sudden their argument that morning assumed

146

minute proportions. All that mattered was her need of him and the desire to know the full extent of his injuries.

'You cannot see him, Dominique,' said Frederick Rivas gently. 'He is at present in a helicopter – on his way to Rio de Janeiro, to the hospital there. They are much more adequately equipped to deal with his injuries than the hospital in Bela Vista.'

'But what are his injuries?' exclaimed Dominique desperately. 'Senhor Rivas – please!'

'Well, he has been burned!' said Frederick Rivas bluntly. 'There was an explosion—'

'An explosion!' murmured Dominique incredulously. 'But how did that happen? How *could* that happen?'

'That's what I intend to find out,' replied Rivas grimly. 'However, for the present I will concentrate on Vincente. He was conscious when he left and it was at his insistence that I did not ring you sooner. He did not want you to dash to the refinery in a panic as no doubt you would have done.'

Dominique felt a cold hand round her heart. Even when he was injured, probably in pain, he had not wanted her around. He had not *needed* her! That hurt. That really hurt!

'Yes,' she said now, a little dully. 'So – so what must I do?' Her voice shook, much to her annoyance.

'Well,' Rivas sounded rather uncomfortable now, 'well – Dominique, if I were you, I would wait until this evening, and ring the hospital in Rio. They will be able to give you all the details.'

Dominique felt sick. 'But – but – I want to see him,' she exclaimed. 'I – I must see him!'

'I do not think he wants you to see him just now, Dominique,' said Rivas cautiously. 'These burns that I mentioned – they are about the face. I must tell you – I must *warn* you, Dominique – Vincente has been badly burned!'

Dominique shook her head impatiently. 'Do – do you think I care about that? Do you think I care what he looks like? Do you think I would feel repelled? Oh, Senhor Rivas, I love him! I – I would love him if he looked like – like – like a monster!'

'Are you sure, Dominique? Vincente was a very attractive man—'

Dominique noticed that he said 'was'. She felt an awful sense of impatience.

'Of course I'm sure,' she said now. 'Senhor, give me the name of this hospital. Let me decide for myself what I must do.'

'It is the Hospital of Saint Augustine,' replied Rivas slowly. 'But wait, Dominique. One moment. Give yourself time to think.'

'To think? About what?'

'Vincente does not wish that you should rush to see him. This much was obvious from his disturbed state before he left. At least give him the chance to accept his injuries.'

Dominique compressed her lips. 'You're asking the impossible, *senhor*.'

'Am I?' Rivas sounded uncomfortable. 'My child, things are not well between you and Vincente, this I know.'

'How do you know that?'

'Last night Vincente came to our house. He had dinner with us. He was very restless – very disturbed. He stayed late – much later than before. This is not the behaviour of a man with a new bride – a bride of only two days. We are not fools, Dominique.'

Dominique heaved a shaky sigh. At least now she knew where he had been! All her stupid imaginings had been for nothing. Why did she always think the worst of him? Why was she so suspicious? Had she so little faith? Was her love

148

the puny thing he had said it was?

She gave up this speculation. It was impossible to try and work things out at this time. There were more important issues at stake.

'I'd better go,' she said. 'I – I promise to think over all you've said. I can't promise more than that.'

'Well, that's something,' said Rivas approvingly. 'Goodbye, Dominique. And good luck!'

After she had rung off, Dominique said urgently: 'Salvador, how do I find the number of the St. Augustine Hospital in Rio?'

Salvador studied her for a moment. 'You have listened to what Senhor Rivas had to say, *senhora?*'

'Of course. Did he tell you what had happened?'

'Briefly, yes. He said that Senhor Santos was most anxious that you should not attempt to see him without his knowledge.'

Dominique took a step back. 'What do you mean?'

'Senhor Rivas must have told you.'

'Yes, he did. But – you can't agree with him! I mean – well, obviously I've *got* to see him!'

'Why? There is nothing you can do at this time,' asked Salvador impassively. '*Senhora*, do not be precipitate!'

'Oh, you're impossible!' she exclaimed. 'In any case, how could I reach Rio without your assistance? I just want to know how he is. Surely that is permitted.'

'He will barely have arrived, *senhora*. Give them time. Let them examine him. Ring later – after dinner.'

Dominique considered this, then moved restlessly. 'I should have been told when it happened,' she fumed. 'I'm his wife! I had a right to know. To be there. Salvador, surely you of all people must know how I feel!'

'Oh, yes, *senhora*, I, too, would like to know more of what has happened. But we can only wait. There is no other helicopter, and the telephone is at least an immediate link.'

'We have a car,' she reminded him.

'No, *senhora*.' Salvador was firm. He sighed then. '*Senhora*, it is obvious you have never experienced this kind of situation. I was in a civil war once, and with a man when some explosive he was handling blew up in his face. I was lucky. The blast knocked me over and I fell face downwards. My friend was not so lucky. His face was badly injured. It was many months before it was recognizable as a face again. That man could not bear the company of anyone who had known him prior to the accident. Can you not understand that?'

Dominique quivered. 'You don't—you don't imagine Vincente's injuries are *that* severe, do you? Oh, God!' she sank down weakly on to the side of the telephone table.

Salvador clucked his teeth. 'No, *senhora*, I did not say that. I was merely trying to show you that a man who is disfigured in an accident can be very conscious of that disfigurement.'

Dominique shook her head. 'But you're so cool, Salvador! If I didn't know you so well I'd say that you were completely indifferent to what had happened!' She buried her face in her hands.

Salvador's features tautened. 'Do not ever say that, *senhora*,' he said almost angrily, and she looked up at the intense feeling in his voice. 'I – more than anyone – pray that this affair is not as serious as it sounds. But if it is, then it is up to me to be a comfort to you, a support for what may be to come. I cannot show my feelings so blatantly. I have had years of hiding my inmost thoughts. Only with Senhor Santos was I ever myself, and now – with you.'

Dominique felt guilty. 'I'm sorry, Salvador, that was thoughtless of me. I'm truly sorry. I suppose I'm distraught. Oh, what time is it? How much longer until we can ring the hospital, do you suppose?'

'It is a little after five-thirty, *senhora*. I will ask Maurice to prepare dinner for seven this evening. We will ring at eight.'

Dominique nodded. 'All right. All right, Salvador.' She smoothed the sweat from her forehead. 'I think I'll go and take a shower in the meantime.'

'Yes, *senhora*.'

Dominique walked across the lounge, then she looked back. 'Tell me one thing, Salvador, what was she like? The other woman Vincente married?'

Salvador bent his head. 'She was – a woman,' he replied. Then he looked up. 'This is not my affair, *senhora*.'

'Salvador!'

'She was a beautiful woman, powerful and rich, and older than Senhor Santos.'

Dominique halted, fascinated. 'Go on.'

Salvador looked as though he would refuse, then he sighed. 'Her name was Valentina Cordova. But it was many years ago. Many things have happened since then.'

'Were they divorced?'

Salvador frowned. 'Divorced? No! Senhora Santos died.'

Dominique swallowed hard. 'She died?' she echoed disbelievingly.

'Yes, *senhora*.'

'But why? She was not so old, surely.'

'No, *senhora*. She was about as old as Senhor Santos is now.'

'Then how—' Dominique stared at him.

But Salvador shook his head. '*Senhora*, I have told you about the other wife of the Senhor. I have told you her name, and I have told you she died. I do not wish to talk any more about it. I have already said too much.'

Dominique sighed, but she did not feel she should press him no matter how curious she felt. At least she had the satisfaction of knowing that her predecessor had not been cast aside in the divorce court. What had Marion said? She hadn't actually said that he had divorced his previous wife. She had merely allowed that assumption to be made.

Giving Salvador a faintly grateful smile, she began to climb the stairs to her room. And as she did so the full enormity of what Frederick Rivas had just told her swept over her. Until now she had been so anxious, trying to find out how soon she could see him she had not actually given a great deal of thought to the state of his injuries, and what burning might entail. To imagine him in great pain, lying alone in that hospital in Rio, with no one to love or care for him, tore her heart into shreds. Whatever he had done, she longed to see him again. Tomorrow, no matter what excuses Salvador might offer, she would go to the hospital of St. Augustine.

CHAPTER NINE

DOMINIQUE scarcely touched her dinner, but she was moved at the way Maurice, the chef, and his wife came to say how sorry they were that Senhor Santos had been injured. Afterwards Salvador got the number of the hospital and the call was put through.

The specialist who had been summoned to deal with the case answered the telephone, and he was able to tell Dominique something of what to expect. Apparently Vincente was injured mainly on one side of his face and there was some concern about his left eye which had been scorched. Dominique winced as the surgeon described the injuries involved, and the extent of the damage.

'The burns are classed as first degree burns,' he said, clearly, 'although they verge on something more serious. However, there is no possible reason why skin grafts should not take place as soon as the patient is able to take the operations involved, and later, in perhaps six months or a year at most, plastic surgery can eradicate any scarring.'

Dominique listened intently. 'But how is he, doctor?' she asked tremulously. 'Is he in pain?'

'Not at present, *senhora*. He is under sedation, and there are drugs we can prescribe to alleviate unnecessary suffering. Your husband is a healthy man. There is no reason why he should not recover completely.'

'When – when can I see him?' Dominique could not prevent the question.

The doctor hesitated. 'I believe Senhor Santos prefers that you do not see him yet,' he said, with some concern. 'However, it is my own personal opinion that it is better to

153

face this kind of thing at once, and to delay the inevitable is hardly conducive to recovery in the patient. Obviously he is very conscious that he looks – well, much different. Senhora Santos, do you want to see your husband?' This last was said rather abruptly.

'Of course.'

'Then come, by all means. I have the feeling he is in rather a depressed state just at the moment. It may be that your presence will remove his tension.'

Dominique wondered whether she ought to tell the doctor something of the situation between herself and Vincente and then stifled the thought. Vincente would hate the idea of any stranger being told of his private affairs.

After she had rung off Salvador said: 'You are going?'

'Tomorrow,' she nodded. 'Will you take me?'

Salvador shrugged. 'Of course. But I hope you are not making a mistake.'

'I've got to see him,' she replied blankly, and he nodded.

In the morning she dressed with care, choosing a slim-fitting suit of navy blue silk, edged with white. The skirt was short and had an inverted pleat at the front, while the jacket was box-shaped with three-quarter sleeves. She plaited her hair into its coronet and then studied her reflection critically. She looked cool and detached, and she prayed she could maintain that appearance.

It was quite an experience driving to Rio. She had not been through the mountains before by road, and the steep passes and precipices took her mind from the ordeal in front of her. For it was an ordeal, contemplating what Vincente's reaction might be. If he was furiously angry with her, she thought she would die.

They reached Rio before noon, and drove at once to the hospital. It was a huge modern building, and inside it was clinically white and impersonal. Dominique thought that life and death passed side by side along these corridors and she shivered at the realization. She had never felt so fanciful before.

The reception desk was occupied by a white-clad assistant who immediately contacted a doctor by telephone and Dominique waited impatiently for him to come to speak with her. She had asked Salvador to accompany her, but when the doctor appeared, and invited her into a small office that opened off the entrance hall, Salvador held back, and Dominique went in alone.

The doctor introduced himself as Manoel Verrez, and after Dominique had seated herself he explained that he was in charge of her husband's case in a general way. The specialist who had treated his injuries the previous evening and the surgeon who would perform the skin grafts were at present occupied with their work, and he had been detailed to put her in the picture.

Dominique listened as he explained that Vincente was recovering quite satisfactorily from the shock of the explosion, and that although a dressing had been put on his eye, his cheek was exposed to the air which might be rather harrowing for Dominique to see.

'He is in the intensive care unit,' went on Doctor Verrez. 'It is a special plastic unit attached to the hospital and is used to dealing with cases of this kind.'

'How long will he be in hospital?' asked Dominique.

'Hmmm!' Doctor Verrez cupped his chin with his hand. 'I am not certain. Four – maybe five weeks in all. And then later he will return for the plastic surgery.'

'Is – is that necessary?' asked Dominique faintly.

'Plastic surgery? No, it is not necessary! But we find it is the usual progression of a case of this kind.'

Dominique shook her head. 'So much surgery,' she murmured, almost to herself. 'So many operations! Oh, Doctor

Verrez, can I see him?'

The doctor smiled. 'I do not see why not. Does he know you are coming?'

'Actually – no. But the specialist I spoke with last evening suggested that it might be a good idea if I came.'

'Very well. Come. We will go up to the private ward where he is at present. Come!'

Salvador remained in the reception hall while Dominique entered the lift and rode up to the third floor with Doctor Verrez. Her heart was beating rapidly, and she felt almost sick with apprehension.

They walked along a white-tiled corridor to a room at the far end, but before entering it they entered the Ward Sister's office. She looked up and smiled when she saw Doctor Verrez. He introduced Dominique, and the Sister viewed her with rather disturbed eyes.

'I do not believe your husband is prepared for your reactions to his injuries yet, Senhora Santos,' she said carefully. 'And at the moment he has a visitor.'

Dominique's heart sank. 'A visitor?' she echoed blankly, wondering who this might be. Could it be Sophia? Or even Claudia? Or someone she had yet to meet?

'But yes,' said Sister Sanchez calmly. 'It is the Senhorita Santos, the Senhor's sister.'

'Isabella!' exclaimed Dominique, in surprise. 'But I thought—'

The Sister nodded. 'You are thinking that she is a novice at the convent, are you not?'

'Well, yes.'

'Apparently the Mother Superior has granted her special dispensation to visit with her brother. After all, apart from yourself, she is his only living relative, is she not?'

Dominique turned scarlet. She didn't know. *She didn't know.*

156

'I – I—' she began unhappily, when Doctor Verrez said:

'Perhaps it would be as well if Senhora Santos went in while Senhorita Santos is there,' he suggested. 'After all, it will be less of an ordeal for both of them that way.'

'Of course. That might be a good idea,' agreed Sister Sanchez. 'Would you like me to accompany you, *senhora*?'

Dominique shook her head. 'No. No, that won't be necessary. Will – will you show me which room . . .'

The door was straight ahead, at the foot of the corridor, and nodding her thanks to the Sister and to Doctor Verrez, Dominique walked slowly to the door. Then, with determined efforts, she turned the handle and entered the room.

At first, she was terrified, not only of Vincente's anger, but of her own inadequacy. She was afraid she might be unable to prevent herself from showing some emotion, some faint revulsion, at the sight of his scarred face. But she found that she was only conscious of a sense of relief that he was there, alive, and his injuries, ugly though they appeared, were nothing compared to the surge of love and anxiety she felt for him and him alone.

He was lying against his pillows, dressed in dark pyjamas that darkened his already swarthy complexion, and threw into prominence the pale, livid flesh of the left side of his face. As the doctor had warned her his eye was concealed by a dressing, while the rest of his face had reddened patches of skin where the explosion had slightly scorched it. Thankfully, his forehead and nose were unscathed, and in consequence his hair had not had to be cut back.

At her entrance the girl who was sitting at the far side of the bed rose to her feet, but Dominique was only conscious of her as a dark-robed figure; her attention was centred on

Vincente. His good right eye was immediately turned in her direction, and as she watched she saw his face register a procession of emotions, most powerful of them all being a violent angry rejection of her presence.

'*Por Dios*, Dominique!' he muttered furiously. 'What are you doing here? I told them to tell you not to come!'

Dominique almost shrank back from the anger in his voice. 'Vincente—' she began unsteadily, unsure as to whether her traitorous emotions might betray her once again.

The girl, whom Dominique recognized from the photograph in Vincente's apartment, said: 'Your wife has the right to see you – to comfort you, Vincente,' in a calm, gentle voice.

Dominique glanced at her and then returned her gaze to her husband. Vincente, who had moved restively when he saw his wife, sank back against his pillows as though exhausted by the effort, and said harshly:

'Dominique has no rights as far as I am concerned!'

Dominique stared at him incredulously, then Vincente's sister moved round the bed to her side, and said: 'I am Isabella Santos, Vincente's sister.'

Dominique summoned all her small store of composure. 'Yes – yes, I know. I – I'm only sorry we had to meet in such circumstances.'

Isabella smiled. She was very calm, very composed, and very beautiful in the plain robes of a novice.

'Come,' she said. 'Sit down. I am just leaving.'

'*No!*' Vincente's voice was imperative. 'Isabella, please. Stay!'

Dominique twisted the strap of her handbag tightly. 'I – I think perhaps I ought to go,' she began awkwardly, aware that she could not stand much more of Vincente's antagonism. Not after the emotional strain she had been suffering.

'Nonsense!' exclaimed Isabella sharply. 'My brother is too conscious of himself. He is under the false impression that appearances are everything.'

'Isabella! For God's sake,' muttered Vincente wearily. 'Can't you see she's positively dying to get away again? Not that I blame her. I'm sure my face is enough to make anyone feel positively sick!'

'That's not true!' cried Dominique, turning to him. 'Do you honestly think I care what you look like! Heavens, I'm only glad that you are alive!'

'I find that hard to believe,' said Vincente roughly. 'Surely things would have been much simpler for you if I had been killed!'

'Oh!' Dominique pressed a hand to her lips. 'How can you say such things?'

Isabella gave her brother an impatient glance. 'Stop it, Vincente! Can't you see Dominique is practically at the end of her tether? It must have been a terrible shock for her—'

'Get out! Both of you!' muttered Vincente, sliding down on his pillows and staring at the ceiling of the small private ward. 'I'm tired.'

Dominique looked at Isabella, and with a faint sigh and a shake of her head Isabella indicated that they should do as he suggested so brutally.

Outside in the corridor, Dominique broke down completely, and Doctor Verrez who appeared just then looked very disturbed.

'Senhora Santos!' he exclaimed, in astonishment. 'Was his appearance such a shock to you? I did warn you—'

'Oh, no,' cried Dominique, 'it's not his appearance. I – I can't explain. Excuse me.'

She hurried off down the corridor, and after a few moments Isabella followed her. She put her arm around Dominique, and they entered the lift together.

Downstairs Salvador hurried to meet them, greeting Isabella warmly, and kissing her hand. Isabella spoke with him rapidly in their own language which Dominique simply could not follow, and then Salvador nodded, and with one on either side of her Dominique left the hospital.

They went to the car, and Isabella helped Dominique into the back and then slid in beside her while Salvador got into the front seat as usual.

'Now,' said Isabella, in English, 'we will go to a hotel I know here in Rio. Once there we can talk, and maybe salvage something from this mess.'

Dominique nodded, and leaned back against the upholstery of the car weakly. In all her vain imaginings she had not really believed Vincente would reject her so completely. It wasn't only his appearance, she was sure. He could no longer bear the sight of her.

They went to the Hotel Maria Magdalena, and Dominique tried to forget the memories this hotel invoked. Was it only three weeks since she had arrived in Brazil so light-heartedly? So many things had happened that it seemed like a lifetime ago!

Isabella, with some of her brother's assurance, arranged for a suite of rooms to be put at their disposal for the afternoon. Then Salvador departed about some business of his own and the two girls went up in the lift to their apartments.

It was very hot, and already most of the populace were indulging in the usual afternoon siesta. But Dominique did not feel tired, although she had a severe headache, and would have appreciated some time alone to collect herself. However, Isabella seemed to sense this for she suggested that Dominique might like to rest in one of the bedrooms while she arranged for some lunch to be served in the suite.

Dominique insisted she wanted nothing to eat, but when Isabella tapped on her door later and produced a tray of light snacks and sandwiches, accompanied by fresh fruit and coffee, she managed to swallow some of the food and immediately felt better equipped to face what was to come.

Isabella seemed disposed to talk, and seated herself on the end of the bed and said, rather disconcertingly: 'What has happened between you and Vincente? Why is he so antagonistic towards his bride of only three days?'

Dominique put away her coffee cup and reached for her cigarettes. 'Didn't he tell you?' she asked, putting a cigarette between her lips and lighting it with rather shaky fingers.

'No,' replied Isabella calmly. 'If he had done so I should not be asking you. I am not being unnecessarily curious. It's just that – well, I love my brother, and I do not like to see him so unhappy.'

'Unhappy?' echoed Dominique. 'He's not unhappy. At least, that wasn't the impression I gained. He – he seems to *hate* me!'

'Oh, I think not,' exclaimed Isabella sharply. 'I do know my brother perhaps rather better than you do. I can tell when – well, I believe he is brooding about something. Can't you – couldn't you tell me?'

Dominique sighed. How could she explain to Isabella about their row? How could she tell her that it was to do with her – with her and John Harding?

Finally she said: 'I – he didn't tell me he had been married before.'

'I see.' Isabella nodded. 'Tell me something, Dominique, how long did you know my brother – before you married him?'

Dominique flushed. 'Not very long.'

'It was an instant attraction, then?'

'You could say that,' agreed Dominique cautiously.

'And so I suppose you got to know very little about one another – about one another's affairs – before you actually got married.'

'That's right.'

'What do you actually know about Vincente? Do you know his background?'

Dominique stared at her. 'No. I know nothing – absolutely nothing. Oh, it's difficult to explain – I expect it sounds completely crazy to you, but – well, words were not important between us. Not then. And after—' She sighed. 'We didn't have time. I only know what Salvador has told me. Will you tell me about Vincente? Will you tell me how he became what he is? When I arrived here, he seemed violently aroused when I discussed the poverty of some of the people, and later he made some remark about not having always known this kind of life. I didn't understand him, and he wouldn't explain. Will you?'

Isabella rose to her feet and paced to the window, staring pensively out at the view. Then she looked back at Dominique and smiled.

'I'll tell you a little,' she offered quietly. 'I will tell you what I think you should know.'

'Yes?' Dominique was expectant.

'Yes.' Isabella sighed. 'To begin with, Vincente and I are not – how shall I put it? – er – solitary children. Hmm, we have brothers and sisters, but we do not know them.'

Dominique stared at her in surprise. 'What do you mean?'

Isabella shrugged. 'Our parents were very poor. There were, I believe, nine of us. But our parents could not afford to keep us, and we ran the streets, like those children you saw in the *favellas*, yes?'

'Yes.'

'You do not know what it is like to be poor, I can see that. Believe me, I do not mean to sound patronizing, but unless one has experienced that kind of existence, one cannot understand the complete and utter degradation of not having shoes or clothes, or even combs for our hair. We were thin and ragged, but we were together, Vincente and I. He was much older than me, of course, and much wiser, I am sure.' She smiled. 'One day a man came to the *favellas*. He was a business man. My father had been working for one of his companies, and he had stolen some money. The man threatened to call the police. My father begged and pleaded, he told him he had a large family to support, and that we would starve if he was taken away.'

She sounded slightly bitter, and Dominique realized that their father had not been entirely truthful in his estimation of his value to the rest of the family.

'At any rate,' she went on, 'the man must have had a heart, because he looked at us and he smiled. It was a beautiful smile, and Vincente smiled at him. I was too frightened to do anything but hide behind Vincente. The man came to Vincente, and he asked my father what was his name. My father said that he was his eldest son. It was not true, but my father thought the man might feel more strongly towards the eldest son, might think my father had more to lose. We did not know what was in his mind. It was not until later that we found that this man, this Senhor Santos, had a wife who could not have children of her own. Senhor Santos wanted to adopt Vincente. There was money to change hands, and my father was a greedy man. Unfortunately, Vincente refused to go unless I was to go also. I say, unfortunately, because I seem to have caused my brother nothing but trouble.' She sighed again.

Dominique was beginning to understand. 'How – how old

163

was Vincente then?' she asked.

'He was eleven, and I was three. That was twenty years ago now.'

Dominique shook her head. 'Did you ever see your real parents again?'

Isabella shook her head. 'They moved – we did not know where, and I suppose now they are dead.' She said this dispassionately, and Dominique stared at her.

'Did you have no feeling for them – not even your mother?' she exclaimed.

Isabella shrugged. 'My mother was completely ruled by my father. And I think she had so many children she was glad to see two go.'

'But that's terrible!'

'That is life, Dominique.'

'Is – is that why Vincente is so bitter?'

'Partly, I suppose. At least it may account in some part for his perhaps unreasonable standards.'

'I see,' Dominique nodded. 'And his wife?'

'Valentina?'

'Yes. Did he love her?'

Isabella shook her head. 'That also was a farce. Valentina Cordova was the owner of a huge chain of companies. They had belonged to her father, and when he died she took over the reins. She was a completely ruthless business woman, and everyone said she had no heart. She wanted the Santos Corporation, and she would have got it, too, had not my adopted father begged Vincente to intervene. Vincente was only twenty-two at that time, and Valentina was easily thirty-three or four. But, as you may have realized, he can be completely irresistible if he so chooses, and he disarmed the harsh business woman almost overnight. That he had to marry her to complete the deal was an indication of Valentina's own strength of will.'

'You mean – you mean – that was why he married her?'

'Yes.' Isabella sighed. 'My father was delighted. It was what he had wanted. Vincente knew that. And after all, it was the least he could do for the man who had made him his heir.'

Dominique shook her head. 'It seems incredible! Was – was the marriage a success?'

'If you mean was Valentina happy, then yes, I suppose she was. Whether Vincente was happy or not is debatable. I fear it was another example to him of how people use other people.'

'But he was using Valentina!'

'On our father's behalf only. Our father was a sick man. He urged Vincente to do it, and Vincente obliged. He was indifferent, you see. And how could Vincente let our father down?'

Dominique stubbed out her cigarette, her mouth dry. If Vincente had married once for money, could he have married a second time for revenge? It seemed possible – even probable, and the idea appalled her.

'She died,' she said now, sliding off the bed. 'How?'

'Valentina went to visit with her uncle and aunt in New Orleans. The plane crashed on take-off on her return journey.'

'Oh.' Dominique swallowed hard. 'How convenient for him!'

'You do not mean that,' said Isabella shrewdly. 'And I get the feeling that there is more to this rift between you and Vincente than his previous marriage. Try to understand, Dominique, Vincente's life has not been easy – or uncomplicated, as yours has probably been until now. First there was our life in the *favellas*, when we lived by our wits. And then our life with the Santos's who were really so much

165

more real parents to us, but for Vincente even this affair had its complications, in the form of Valentina. And finally myself. I – well, I got involved with a man, and – well, that is of no interest to you, I am sure. At any rate, Vincente was very shocked when I decided to enter the convent. He tried to dissuade me, but I was adamant.'

Dominique bit her lip. If only she could ask Isabella about that affair, that involvement. If only Isabella would ask what brought her to Brazil in the first place. But obviously Isabella did not realize that Dominique was anything more than an attractive female Vincente had chosen to make his wife.

Conversation dwindled after a while. Both girls seemed absorbed with their own thoughts, and Dominique decided her best plan would be to return to Bela Vista tomorrow, after attempting a second time to speak to Vincente. She voiced this suggestion to Isabella, and she said:

'I think it might be a good idea. It also occurs to me that Vincente might be transferred to the Bela Vista hospital after the skin grafts have taken place.'

Dominique frowned. 'You think so?'

'Why not? And later, when he is recovered, he could stay at Minha Terra, providing there was a nurse . . .'

Dominique frowned again. She did not relish the thought of bringing another woman into her husband's life. But there was no reason to refuse, no *logical* reason.

'Yes,' she agreed doubtfully. 'What – what will you do?'

'Me?' Isabella shrugged. 'I do not know. The convent is some distance from Rio de Janeiro. It would be impossible for me to see him if I were to return there, particularly once he is transferred to Bela Vista.'

'Then – then couldn't you come and stay at Minha Terra?' suggested Dominique, with some impulsiveness.

With Isabella at Minha Terra she might feel a sense of security, and just now that was what she badly needed.

In the evening, when Isabella went to see Vincente, Dominique asked Salvador to take her for a drive. They drove out of the city, to one of the many beauty spots overlooking the bay. The lights winked from the vessels out there, in the ocean, and Dominique obtained a measure of peace from the sense of infinity that the scene presented. She turned to Salvador and said:

'Did you go and see Vincente this afternoon?'

Salvador half smiled. 'Is that a guess – or an assumption?'

'A guess.'

Salvador chuckled. 'You are right, *senhora*. I went to see the Senhor.'

'And?'

'And what?'

'Oh, Salvador, what happened? Did he mention me? Was he angry with you for bringing me?'

'Angry, yes. With you – I do not think so?' Salvador sighed. 'You do not try to understand the Senhor, *senhora*. If he were this Senhor Harding, how would you treat him? Would you be suspicious of his every move? Would you accuse him of deceiving you, on the strength of gossip heard from a known harridan? Would you deliberately torment him by disobeying his every command?'

Dominique frowned. 'I don't understand, Salvador.'

'Of course you do. Tell me, what would you do?'

'It's different with John,' she eventually said, slowly. 'He – he's not like Vincente. He's more – more reliable.'

'You think so? Even though you know he deliberately set out to attract the Senhorita Isabella, and succeeded in breaking her heart?'

167

Dominique stared at him. 'You can't be certain of that!'

'Oh, yes, *senhora*. I was there. I saw it happen. Isabella was a sweet, innocent creature. Your Senhor Harding cared nothing for her. He wanted a flirtation – an affair. Her dark beauty after the fairness of English women attracted him. Oh, yes, *senhora*, I can tell you this now. He was ripe for entertainment, and he chose Isabella as his partner.'

'I don't believe you!' Dominique was aghast. 'We were engaged to be married.'

'Yes. But had you not refused to come with him? Had you not insisted on a longer engagement?'

'How do you know that?'

'Your Senhor Harding is not a silent man, *senhora*. He was morose and dejected, until he met Isabella Santos, at the Santos club. She was there with her brother for some special function. Senhor Harding did not take his eyes from her all evening. He was enchanted by her. You will agree, now that you have met her, that she is a very attractive young woman.'

'Of course.' Dominique brushed back a wisp of hair impatiently. 'Go on.'

'There is little more to tell. Surely you can guess what happened. Isabella fell for your handsome Senhor Harding, and he pretended to fall for her. There was talk of him breaking his engagement, becoming wholly involved with her. But somehow, when it came to the point, he would not do it. The affair – his side of the affair – dissolved into nothing more than that!' Salvador sounded incensed, and Dominique could understand why. These women were not emancipated like Englishwomen. They were not encouraged to deal loosely with any man, except the man who was to be their husband. She could understand Vincente's anger and contempt, and she wondered how John could have done such

168

a thing and continued to write such graphical letters to her.

Sighing, she said: 'But that doesn't alter anything, Salvador. Vincente still hates me!'

Salvador started the car's powerful engine. 'He would like to do so, *senhora*,' he replied enigmatically.

CHAPTER TEN

The following morning Dominique was awakened early by the unusual sound of traffic in the adjoining main street. Sliding out of bed, she walked to the windows and stared out pensively at the misty haze rising over the city, and the distant shimmer of the ocean. It was going to be another perfect day, and she went into the bathroom and hastily sluiced her face and cleaned her teeth before dressing in the navy suit. Their unexpected stay in Rio had found her unprepared, and it was all she had to wear.

Then, opening her door, she silently crossed the lounge of the suite so as not to disturb Isabella, and went out quietly. She took the lift down to the ground floor and smiled at the startled glances the hotel porters gave her.

Outside there was still a chill in the air, but it was heavenly fresh, and she walked slowly, allowing the faint breeze to blow away the cobwebs from her mind.

At the junction with the main road she beckoned a taxi, and when one halted she asked the driver to take her to the St. Augustine Hospital. Then she settled back on the back seat, and hoped her faint feeling of hopefulness would strike some matching chord in Vincente's heart.

The hospital was already busily active, and she was allowed to go straight up to the third floor where Vincente's room was situated. Sister Sanchez was no longer on duty, instead it was Sister Moreno, and she looked rather surprised when Dominique introduced herself.

'But Senhor Santos is barely awake,' she exclaimed. 'We do not rouse our private patients before seven-thirty. It is only seven-forty-five now.'

Dominique was impatient. 'I'm his wife, Sister Moreno,' she said. 'Surely the time is less than important. How is he today?'

'Improving satisfactorily,' replied Sister Moreno smoothly. 'It should not be much longer before we begin the skin grafts.'

'And he's going to be all right?'

'Of course. Perhaps there will be some scarring to begin with. But later – with plastic surgery – he will be completely recovered.'

'Can I see him, then?'

'If you insist, but it is most irregular,' replied Sister Moreno shortly.

Dominique shrugged, thanked her, and left her office to enter the private ward where Vincente was accommodated. She tapped at the door, waited for his curt summons, and entered the room. Vincente stared at her disbelievingly, then said: 'Why have you come? Where is Isabella?'

'Asleep at the hotel, I imagine,' replied Dominique, more calmly than she felt. 'How are you this morning?'

'As well as can be expected,' he returned coldly, turning so that the injured side of his face was partially hidden from her sight.

Dominique closed the door and approached the bed. 'Tell me,' she said, 'what happened at the plant? How did the explosion take place?'

'That's something I shall find out when I'm out of this place,' he said tersely. 'Have they told you how long they expect to keep me here?'

'No. But Isabella said she thought they would probably transfer you to Bela Vista once the skin grafts had taken place.'

'But how long?' He was staring moodily down at the coverlet. She could have been anyone.

'Altogether, perhaps a month – six weeks, even.' She came round the bed to his side. 'Why?'

'Because there are things I must do,' he replied harshly.

He stared at her for a moment, and her eyes flickered over the burned flesh of his face without revulsion. There was no feeling of distaste in her. He was the man she loved, and all she felt was a surge of protective emotion.

However, Vincente seemed to sense none of this. Instead he said: 'Why did you come? Wasn't yesterday enough for you?'

'Yesterday you wouldn't speak to me,' she said unsteadily. 'And I need to talk to you. Isabella has told me about Valentina.'

His face darkened. 'Oh, indeed! Did she also unburden herself about Harding?'

'No. She doesn't know I know John.'

'Of course not. I had forgotten. Perhaps you had better not mention him. After all, you are hardly the person she would most like to meet.'

'I didn't intend to mention it. Besides, John's affairs are nothing to do with me.'

'Aren't they? Don't you wish you'd married him after all? At least he would have had more sense than to—' He halted abruptly, and she wondered what it was he had been going to say.

'I married you because I loved you,' she replied shakily.

'Is that so? I notice you use the past tense.'

'Stop trying to trip me. Why did you marry me? That's a much more complex question, isn't it?' Her voice almost broke and she swallowed hard.

Vincente lay back on his pillows regarding her steadily. 'You will never know why I married you,' he said cruelly. 'Because I do not intend to tell you. That's something for you to think about – to take your mind off *this*!' He pointed momentarily at his cheek, and then rolled on to his stomach, propping himself up on his elbows. 'Now get out, I don't want to see you any more.'

'Vincente, stop it!' she cried. 'You've obviously never been jealous, or you couldn't act like this.'

He turned on to his back. 'Is that what you are saying? That you were jealous?' He sounded sardonic.

Dominique moved restlessly. 'Yes – yes, of course.'

Vincente gave a derogatory smile. 'My God!' he said bitterly. 'How you can twist things! You had absolutely nothing to be jealous of.'

'I know that now – but – well, even the day we were married, you set out to tantalize me!'

Vincente sat up, his face serious. 'That was different,' he said coldly. 'I – I wanted you then!'

'And you don't want me now?' Dominique pressed her hands to her cheeks.

'Not in the same way,' he replied humiliatingly.

Dominique stared at him, unable to believe that he could have changed so utterly, and yet there was cruelty and bitterness in every line of his face. With a muffled sob she turned and dashed to the door, opening it fumblingly, and rushing away down the corridor, ignoring the startled stares of the nurses and orderlies who passed her. Once she heard her name called, but she would not go back, and when she glanced back and saw Vincente himself standing in the doorway of his room, watching her, she quickened her step, reaching the lift, and closing the gates with panic-stricken movements. It was not until she was in the taxi, going back to the hotel, that she allowed the hot tears to flood her cheeks and drown her misery.

Isabella was having breakfast when Dominique returned

to the hotel. But when she saw Dominique's tear-reddened eyes and strained expression she forbore to ask where she had been. Obviously she could guess. Instead, she told Dominique that she had contacted the Mother Superior at the convent and she had decided to take her up on her offer to return to Minha Terra for a while.

'I am sure it is a good idea,' she said, in her usual calm tones. 'I can easily have Salvador drive me down to Rio to see Vincente, until such time as he is transferred to Bela Vista. I will ask about that this morning.'

Dominique merely nodded, giving a faint smile, and went to bathe her face.

Later in the day, after Isabella had visited Vincente again, they drove back to Bela Vista with Salvador. Isabella seemed absorbed with her thoughts, and once or twice she began to say something to Dominique, only to prevent herself at the last moment.

And so began for Dominique the longest and most miserable month of her life. Just as Isabella had said, Vincente was transferred to the Bela Vista hospital ten days later, and continued to make rapid progress. Isabella visited him almost every day, but she did not question Dominique's decision not to visit him again, even though Dominique had been sure she would do so. Indeed, Dominique had sometimes hoped Isabella would make some effort to persuade her sister-in-law to visit the hospital, if only to give her a reason to go there, for although she said she did not want to go, not seeing Vincente was having a terrible effect on her nerves. She questioned Isabella extensively about the skin grafting and his other injuries, and rang the hospital frequently herself and spoke to his doctor.

If the hospital staff were amazed that she should never visit, they must have put it down to her natural revulsion against ugliness, and although this disturbed her, she would

174

not give in and go and have Vincente hurt and humiliate her once again. There would be time enough for that once he came home again. And it was this time that she anticipated and yet feared most.

Sometimes she wished he would finish with her completely, give her a divorce on any grounds he cared to name, but mostly she knew that if he did that she would never be the same again. Life with Vincente might be stormy, but life without him was no life at all.

During Vincente's third week in hospital, Frederick Rivas came to visit Dominique. Isabella was at the hospital at the time, and Dominique invited him in warmly, glad of someone new to talk to. She had avoided going down to the town because she was aware of the talk and speculation which would be rife there.

'How are you?' Frederick asked gently. 'You have lost much weight, Dominique. Are you finding the strain too much?'

Dominique managed a smile. 'I'm fine, thank you,' she replied. 'As you say – it is a strain, but – I – I believe he is very well.'

'Vincente?' Frederick shrugged. 'He is rapidly recovering. I saw him only yesterday. In fact – in fact that is why I am here.'

Dominique stiffened. 'Oh – oh, yes?'

Already her nerves were jumping at the mention of his name, and she walked jerkily across to the bell and summoned Salvador, and asked him to bring her and Senhor Rivas some hot chocolate. Then, lighting a cigarette to calm herself, she said:

'Do go on, Senhor Rivas.'

'Oh, Frederick, please,' he exclaimed, and she nodded and smiled. 'So', he said, 'you have not been to see your husband since he returned to Bela Vista.'

175

Dominique compressed her lips. 'That's right,' she said tautly.

'Why?' Frederick frowned. 'Does it distress you so?'

Dominique shook her head, not trusting herself to speak for a moment. 'No. No, it's not that. It's just that – well – oh, what's the use?' She bit her bottom lip to stop it trembling. 'You may as well know, Senhor – I mean, Frederick; my husband doesn't want to see me.'

'You cannot be serious!'

'Oh, but I am. And now do you mind if we don't discuss it any more? It – it – well, it upsets me.'

'I can understand that. But you are wrong. Vincente does want to see you. He is chafing at the need for him to stay in the hospital so long when he so urgently wishes to speak with you!'

'Oh, no, you're making a mistake,' replied Dominique, her eyes unnaturally bright. 'Now – here's Salvador. Salvador, put it here, please.'

After Salvador had left them, and she had handed Rivas his chocolate, he said: 'What makes you so certain, Dominique?'

'That – that's rather a private matter,' she replied, awkwardly. 'I'd rather not discuss it.'

'But nevertheless, Vincente does wish to see you. I was there when he asked Isabella again why she had not brought you with her.'

Dominique got to her feet. 'I – I – was there anything else? I mean – I don't want to rush you away, but – well, it's no use! I do not intend to visit my husband, and that's that.'

Rivas looked taken aback, but he made no further mention of it, merely studying her strangely, whenever he thought she was not aware of it. But Dominique was aware of it, and aware of his rather impatient attitude with her. He didn't believe her any more than she believed him. And if Vincente had pretended he wanted to see her to make believe that things were all right between them again, then that was his affair. She would have no part of it. She would not go down there and pretend to be his devoted and loving wife just to satisfy the minds of his friends.

Even so, after Rivas had taken his departure, she wondered why Isabella never mentioned anything of this to her. After all, she must know why Dominique was not going to see Vincente, and she could have told her. But perhaps she thought that it would be cruel to tell her something that was almost certainly pretence.

During the next few days she had several calls from associates of Vincente's at the plant, all inquiring about his health, and she thought that possibly Frederick Rivas thought to shame her into visiting the hospital and finding out about her husband for herself.

Then, one afternoon, she had another visitor. Isabella was resting, and Dominique was alone on the patio when she heard the sound of a car in the courtyard. Going through the lounge she looked out and saw John Harding extricating himself from behind the driving wheel of his vehicle. Her eyes wide, she watched him walk across the courtyard to join her, and couldn't suppress a kind of pleasure in seeing him again. After all, he was her countryman, and once they had been very close to one another.

'Hello, Dom,' he said, smiling warmly. 'It's wonderful to see you again.'

'Hello, John.' Dominique bit her lip. 'What are you doing here?'

John climbed the steps to her side. 'Aren't you going to ask me in for a drink? After all, I know the boss is away.'

Dominique hesitated. There was a sense of betrayal in inviting him into Vincente's house in Vincente's absence.

But then she remembered Isabella, and with a casual gesture, she said: 'Come out to the patio. We can talk there.'

Salvador was on the patio and he stared with blank contempt at Dominique's companion. 'I do not think the Senhor—' he began, only to be silenced by a look from Dominique.

'Bring some iced lime,' she said coolly. 'Please, Salvador.'

'Who is he? Your bodyguard?' asked John sardonically, and lounged into one of the low chairs. 'Come and sit down. I want to talk to you.'

Dominique seated herself as far away from him as she could, and said: 'Yes, and I want to talk to you.'

'Oh? Why?'

'I want to hear about Isabella Santos,' said Dominique bluntly. 'Don't try to deny that you had a – a – flirtation with her.'

John looked taken aback. 'All right, all right, Dominique. I won't lie to you. Yes, I knew Isabella. And yes, I was friendly with her.'

'How friendly?'

'Now look here, I came here to see you, not to hear a tirade about Isabella Santos. All that's in the past.'

'Your past, maybe. Not mine,' retorted Dominique, becoming angry. 'Why have you come here today, anyway? What's made you wait so long?'

'What do you mean?'

'Well, it seems significant that you should come after all this time.'

'I'll tell you why I've come. Yesterday I heard Rivas talking to one of his cronies in the office. He didn't know I was there, but I listened, and guess what I heard? Dominique Santos doesn't visit her husband in the hospital!'

Dominique flushed. 'Oh, I see.'

'Until now I never suspected anything was wrong between you two, but by God! I'm glad I know now.'

'Why?'

'Well, for heaven's sake, it proves what I was afraid of all along. You were infatuated with the guy, you couldn't see that he was only playing you along. I might have known—'

'You know nothing!' cried Dominique, getting unsteadily to her feet. 'How dare you come here and attempt to interfere in my affairs! When I broke our engagement, I made no mistake, John. It's only now I'm beginning to realize what I so nearly invited! Writing to me! Telling me how much you missed me, and all the while you were having an affair with Isabella Santos!'

'It wasn't an affair,' he protested, standing too.

'Then what would you call it, John?' asked a quiet voice from behind them, and Dominique put a hand to her mouth when she saw Isabella standing there, watching them.

'Oh, Isabella!' exclaimed Dominique weakly. 'I'm so sorry you had to hear this!'

Isabella moved into the centre of the patio. 'Well, I'm not, Dominique. I'm glad. It explains so much, so much! Did I understand you aright? You were once John Harding's fiancée? You were the girl he was writing to, in England?'

'That's right,' said Dominique, nodding. 'I – I came here to marry John. But then I met Vincente – and – well, that was it!'

'He deliberately took you away from me,' said John harshly. He looked at Isabella. 'At the time I finished with you' – Isabella flinched slightly at his expression – 'at that time,' he continued, 'I expected to be fired, sent back to England. But your precious brother had a much more subtle plan for revenge, hadn't he? He wouldn't be content with just firing me. He had to destroy my life, take away from me

179

the only girl I ever really loved.'

Dominique's fingers seemed to cling to her lips, and she was holding on to her composure with desperate strength. Put like that, so harshly and so cruelly, it seemed so probable that it almost broke her in two.

But Isabella wasn't finished yet. 'You don't really believe my brother would go to the extent of marrying a woman he didn't love, do you?' she asked John scornfully, with a little of the arrogance her brother sometimes displayed. 'He might have decided to take your girl-friend, he might have planned to do just that. It is the kind of thing Vincente would do. He would keep the vendetta. But he would not marry her. He might make love to her, seduce her, give her to you as a secondhand toy, but not marry her!'

Dominique listened, but it barely went in. She was too absorbed in her own misery. All she could hear was John saying Vincente had married her for revenge. Revenge! The word swung dizzily in her head, and she hardly registered the sound of another car accelerating into the courtyard, and the sudden stillness when the engine was switched off. But the others had heard, and Dominique saw John's face pale a little, while Isabella's flushed with something like anticipation.

There were footsteps, and the sound of Salvador's greeting, then Vincente Santos appeared in the lounge door which opened on to the patio – tall and dark, in a dark suit, his face still showing the scars of the grafting, but nonetheless impressive for all that. Dominique looked astounded, and she stared wildly at Isabella and John. They were all like dummies, carved in some scene from a play, no one moved, no one said anything.

Then, as though on cue, Isabella said: 'So they let you come home after all, Vincente,' as though she had been aware of his imminent arrival.

Vincente stepped on to the patio. He looked completely recovered, and Dominique wondered how long he had been on his feet. Obviously his time in hospital had not been spent wholly in a hospital bed. In fact he looked fit and virile.

John looked at Dominique, and said bitterly: 'Did you know he was coming?'

Dominique shook her head, not trusting herself to speak, and Vincente glanced at her thoughtfully, as though aware of her shaken emotions. Then he looked at John again.

'Why have you come here, Harding?' he asked coldly. 'Can't you leave my wife alone?'

John hunched his shoulders. 'I came because I wanted to tell her that I still love her, and now that you've finished with her, I'm willing to take her back!' He scowled. 'I didn't know you were expected, or I'd have chosen some other time!' He was deliberately provocative, both in his words and his manner.

'Who told you I did not want my wife?' asked Vincente ominously.

'No one told me. I didn't have to be *told*! It's obvious, isn't it? She hasn't exactly run after you while you've been in the hospital! I admire her spirit. It's time someone set down the mighty Santos's. Just as I did when I put you on the floor, where you belong!'

Dominique glanced at Vincente, sensing John's desire to provoke another fight between them. He was standing, fists clenched, but when he spoke his voice was calm and cool, like Isabella's.

'You and I have some unfinished business to attend to, Harding,' he said coldly. 'Down at the refinery.'

John's handsome face turned a brilliant shade of scarlet. 'What the hell do you mean?' he blustered.

'You know damn well what I mean,' replied Vincente

quietly, but with menace in his voice. 'Now – do we go?'

Whether John sensed that this time Vincente was not to be trifled with, Dominique did not know, but he moved awkwardly, thrusting his hands into his pockets, and saying: 'Anything you have to say to me can be said here.'

'Here?' Vincente shook his head. 'I prefer to fight my battles in private.'

'Why?' John seemed to think this was an admission of cowardice. 'Because you're afraid I'll make an ass of you again?'

'You will not do that, Harding,' returned Vincente silkily. 'Do you imagine I could not have defended myself had I so desired it? You are so big, so strong – but so *stupid*! Do you imagine Dominique would have reacted as she did had I decided to retaliate? If I had knocked you unconscious, what do you imagine she would have done? She would have felt pity for you – *for you*! Not for me. And that was something I could not risk.'

'Why, you—' John gasped, all his earlier hostility aroused at this slur against his strength and virility.

He charged towards Vincente, fists clenched, uncaring that his opponent was just out of hospital. Dominique seemed to come to her senses and sprang forward in an effort to get between them, but John thrust her aside, intent on his revenge.

He was big and strong and powerful, but for all that, he was clumsy, and Vincente with his lithe, lean build was far more agile, and certainly more deadly in his intent. As John flailed before him, endeavouring to land a punch, he brought his hand down sharply on the other man's shoulder so that John groaned in rage and lost his guard for a moment. In that moment Vincente brought his fist hard into John's stomach, doubling him up so that it was easy to bring down the deciding chop on the back of his neck. John slumped heavily to the ground, and lay there, inert.

Dominique stared down at him in silence, then looked up into Vincente's face. There was satisfaction there, and something else; a kind of malicious enjoyment.

She shivered. All of a sudden it was too much for her. The weeks of waiting, the continued tension of her relationship with Vincente, and now – this!

With a blind shake of her head, she brushed past Isabella and entered the lounge. In those first seconds she didn't know what she was going to do. It was not until she saw the two cars standing out front that realization came to her.

She had to get away. She could go. There was the means before her, and if she reached Rio it would not be too difficult to contact the British Embassy. As the idea formulated in her mind, she began to hurry, her steps quickening, and finally she ran.

She reached the cars, looked at Vincente's, saw the keys hanging, and slid in. With trembling fingers she started the engine, but it was not so easy to find the gears. She fumbled awkwardly, wasting valuable moments, then found the right one.

But even as the car's wheels began to move, she was conscious of voices shouting, and then Vincente's hands grabbed the car door, and he leant over and pulled the keys out of the ignition before she had time to prevent him.

'I think not,' he said heavily, leaning against the door. 'Your running days are over, Dominique,' and with that he wrenched open the door, and lifted her bodily into his arms.

Dominique struggled, then saw Isabella emerging from the house. She went limp. She was defeated. There was nothing she could do. She must take Vincente's scorn and anger, and accept it.

Isabella reached them, her eyes flashing angrily. 'Have

you taken leave of your senses, Vincente?' she exclaimed. 'Already you have fought a man, and now you attempt to carry Dominique! Are you mad? You will be back in hospital for exhaustion. In God's name, forgive me, but you must tell Dominique about Harding.'

Vincente brushed past Isabella. 'You would have me betray her countryman? Oh, no! I have paid my debt to Harding.'

Isabella followed them, shaking her head, and when they reached the hall they encountered Salvador.

'Please to remove that – that man from the patio, Salvador,' said Vincente commandingly. 'I do not care if you have to take him back to Bela Vista, so long as he is removed immediately.'

'Yes, *senhor*.' Salvador sounded delighted.

Isabella touched her brother's arm. 'I will go with Salvador,' she said quietly. 'I have some shopping to do in Bela Vista.'

'Oh, no,' began Dominique, but Vincente was mounting the stairs, uncaring of the strain of carrying her weight as well as his own.

He took her to their suite and closed the door, then looked at her solemnly, before setting her on her feet again. Dominique rubbed the damp palms of her hands down her dress and said:

'I don't know what your intentions are, Vincente, but I've had just about as much as I can stand.'

'*You* have had just about as much as you can stand!' he echoed incredulously. '*Me* – I have been half out of my mind with anxiety!' His voice was angry suddenly. 'In God's name, Dominique, why did you never come back to the hospital? Why would you never answer the telephone when I rang?'

She stared at him. 'You rang?' she murmured faintly.

'But of course. After you visited me in Rio and left in such a state I rang numerous times, but always Salvador said you were out, or you would not come to the telephone.'

Dominique felt the beginnings of realization dawning on her. She stared at him disbelievingly, then said: 'And Isabella? Did you ask her, too?'

'Of course.'

Dominique shook her head, then turned away. 'Even so – even though I may not have had *all* these messages, why should you want to see me? I mean – you made it plain what you thought of me!'

'Did I?' Vincente sounded bitter. 'I doubt that. To make clear what I think of you would take a lifetime.'

She swung round, pressing her hands together. 'What – what are you trying to say?'

Vincente stared at her, then stepped forward, allowing his hands to slide up her arms to her shoulders, drawing her slowly and irrevocably towards him. He studied her face intently, his dark lashes veiling his eyes, then he said: 'I'm trying, not very successfully, to tell you I love you,' he muttered huskily. 'I know I'm not an easy man to live with – I know I've treated you abominably, but I can't help it. I didn't want to want you – to need you. It's like Marion Rawlings said – I did set out to take you away from Harding. Can you forgive me?'

Dominique stared at him. 'But – but you were so angry . . .' she whispered appealingly.

'I know. I know.' He shook his head, his fingers tightening on her shoulders. 'Can you understand that? Oh, Dominique, it's no use – I've got to do this,' and he pulled her close against him and found her mouth with his own, parting her lips passionately, making her wholly aware of the need inside him.

Dominique felt as though her legs were about to give out on her, when he swung her in his arms and carried her to the bed, kneeling beside it, pressing his lips to her fingers urgently.

Dominique tried to remain coherent. It was difficult when she so badly wanted him to go on making love to her.

'Go – go on,' she murmured.

Vincente sighed, his expression regretful. 'All right, you deserve to know it all,' he murmured achingly. 'When I met you at Galeao, I thought you were a very attractive young woman, and the task I had set myself would prove to be very enjoyable. And it was. Just how enjoyable I was forced to realize. When you fell in the swimming pool that night I think it brought me to the full realization of what had happened. But I couldn't tell you that. God, you were attracted to the glamour – not the man!'

'That's not true—' she began indignantly.

'Not now, perhaps,' he amended softly. 'Now, I'm beginning to believe that there is such a thing as love. I didn't used to. I never wanted to. And when you challenged me, I hated you. Believe me, Dominique, I could have killed you for destroying the faith I was beginning to find.'

Dominique propped herself up. 'But you could have denied it. You could have told me the truth!'

Vincente bent his head. 'I am a proud man, Dominique. That is not a proud confession, it is unfortunately the truth. I could not bear that you should believe that woman before me. I wanted to hurt you, and then – I merely succeeded in hurting myself.'

'But why did you change your mind?'

Vincente sighed. 'That day – that day you ran out of the hospital in Rio, I knew then that I had really hurt you. I wanted to run after you – to plead with you – to tell you I was sorry. But of course I could not. And I never had the chance – until now – to show you I am merely a man who loves you to distraction.'

'Oh, Vincente,' she whispered, and drew him up beside her.

For a while there was silence in the room, and Dominique was content. But later, she stroked his head as it rested on her breast, and said:

'John had something to do with the explosion at the plant, didn't he?'

Vincente shrugged his broad shoulders. 'I don't know.'

'That's not the truth, is it?' she murmured.

'It is over, Dominique,' he replied gently. 'Providing you can stand to live with these scars for a while, I don't care about anything else.'

'But I do.'

Vincente looked up at her, shaking his head. 'Your Mr. Harding is being transferred to the Buenos Aires plant.'

'You could fire him,' she murmured.

'I could not be so unkind to the man who introduced me to the most important woman in my life,' replied Vincente, with satisfaction.

Harlequin Presents Collection

An exciting new series
of early favorites from

Harlequin Presents

This is a golden opportunity
to discover these best-selling beautiful
love stories — available once again
for your reading enjoyment...

because Harlequin understands
how you feel about love.

Harlequin Presents Collection

Available wherever Harlequin books are sold.

GREAT LOVE STORIES NEVER GROW OLD...

Like fine old Wedgwood, great love stories are timeless. The pleasure they bring does not decrease through the years. That's why Harlequin is proud to offer...

HARLEQUIN CLASSIC LIBRARY

Delightful old favorites from our early publishing program!

Each volume, first published more than 15 years ago, is an enchanting story of people in love. Each is beautifully bound in an exquisite Wedgwood-look cover. And all have the Harlequin magic, unchanged through the years!

Two **HARLEQUIN CLASSIC LIBRARY** volumes every month! Available NOW wherever Harlequin books are sold.